Ask About:

W9-CSJ-747

Color Names

Did you know that there are special names that can be used to describe many colors? A dark, purplish red is called crimson. A bright red is called scarlet. Deep blue is named indigo. Emerald is a word used for bright green. Light purple is called lavender. Even white and black have unusual names! Creamy white is called ivory. Ebony is the name for deep, shiny black.

These words are often used to describe the exact way a color looks. Can you think of other special color words?

i	n	d	i	g	o	l
c	e	z	v	l	s	a
r	m	e	x	n	c	v
i	e	b	i	d	a	e
m	r	o	v	i	r	n
s	a	n	o	g	l	d
o	l	y	r	o	e	e
n	d	x	y	b	t	r

Yes or No

Many colors have special names that describe them.   Yes   No

Unscramble, write and circle each new word in the puzzle above.

y o i r v	t r a l s e c	g d n o i i	m l r a e d e
5 3 1 4 2	7 4 3 5 1 6 2	5 3 2 6 1 4	2 6 4 5 1 7 3

d a n r l e v e	m r s c i n o	n y b o e
6 2 5 8 1 4 3 7	4 2 5 1 3 7 6	4 5 2 3 1

Write.

Dark purplish red is called _____.

Bright red is called _____.

Deep blue is called _____.

Bright green is called _____.

Light purple is called _____.

Creamy white is called _____.

• Draw and color a lavender dress and a scarlet umbrella.

1

Ask About:

Shapes

Shapes are all around you. Everyday things are made of different shapes. Kites can be diamond shaped. Balls, wheels and even the Earth are circles. Boxes and tables can be shaped like a square or rectangle. You can find these shapes in many common objects.

There are some unusual shapes that are harder to find in things around you. An egg is an oval. A hexagon has six sides. You can see a hexagon in some road signs. An octagon has eight sides. Can you think of something that is shaped like an octagon?

Name_____

Circle each shape word.

square   circle

hexagon   ? ? ?
                        oval

lunch

triangle

shine

diamond   octagon

octopus
            rectangle

Circle.
Everyday things are made of different   ships.
                                             shapes.

Write.

| circle |
| rectangle |
| oval |
| square |
| triangle |

_____

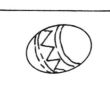

_____

_____

_____

Circle.
A hexagon has   four
                six   sides. An octagon has   eight
                                                six   sides.

Write.   _____   _____

• Draw a red stop sign shaped like a hexagon.

A Diary

Do you think it would be fun to remember just what you did on a certain day two years ago? One way to remember each day is to write about it in a diary. Many people write in their diaries each day. They write about what they did, what they ate, who they saw and what they felt during that day. Most people feel very private about what they write. They do not want anyone else to read their diaries.

Long ago, many people wrote in diaries, too. Some of these old diaries have been found. They are famous because we can learn about life long ago.

Underline.

Writing in a diary   is a way to remember each day.
is like reading a magazine.

Check.

What do many people write about in their diaries each day?

- [ ] What they did that day
- [ ] Who they saw that day
- [ ] Ten math problems
- [ ] How they felt about things that happened that day

Circle.

What does **private** mean in the story?

People do not want anyone to read their diaries.
People feel tired after writing in their diaries.

Write about **your** day in the picture diary.

• Make your own diary. Try writing every day for a week!

The Hand Calendar

Everyone knows that there are twelve months in a year. But do you have trouble remembering how many days are in each month? Some months have 31 days. Some have 30 days. Only February has 28 days.

Your hands can help you tell which are the long or short months. Make a fist with your left hand. Use your right hand to touch the knuckles and the spaces between the knuckles. As you do this, say the name of each month. When you get to the end of your hand, start back at the first knuckle. The long months will be on the knuckles. The short months will be the spaces.

January
February
March
April
May
June
July
August
September
October
November
December

Circle.

There are twelve / twenty months in a year.

Write the month names from the picture on the lines below.

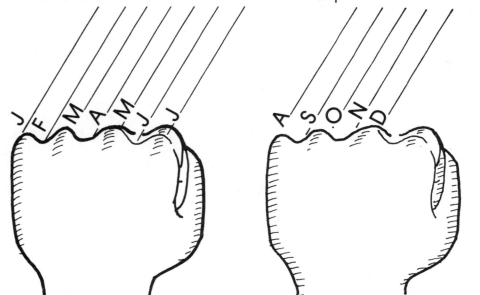

Knuckles = 31 days

Spaces = 30 days

(except February)

Write the number of days in each month in the circles above.
• Draw a calendar page for your birthday month.

Ask About:

The Heart

Have you ever imagined that your heart looked like a valentine? Your heart is really about the size and shape of your fist! Everytime your heart beats it pumps blood to your body. Your heart never rests. It beats 100,000 times a day!

One part of your heart sends blood to all parts of your body. The blood carries oxygen that your body needs to live. The other part of the heart takes the blood coming back from your body. It sends it to your lungs for more oxygen. Then, the fresh blood is pumped back to your body again.

Circle.
Your heart is about the size and shape of a:

   valentine   fist

Yes or No
Your heart pumps blood through your body.	Yes	No
Your heart beats 25 times a day.	Yes	No
Your heart never rests.	Yes	No
Your blood carries oxygen **to** your body.	Yes	No

Underline.
Which blood has oxygen in it?
   The blood which your heart sends out to the body
   The blood which your heart takes back from your body

• Draw a picture which shows your heart pumping blood.

Ask About:

Bones

Have you ever wondered why your body has so many bones? All of the bones in your body form a skeleton. With help from your muscles and joints, the skeleton supports your body and holds it together.

Your body has 206 bones! They are different shapes and sizes. Your arms and legs have long bones. But, your toes and fingers have short bones. Your hipbone is flat. The largest bone in your body is the thighbone. It is in the top part of your leg. The smallest bones are called the hammer, anvil and stirrup. Can you guess where they are? They are in your ears!

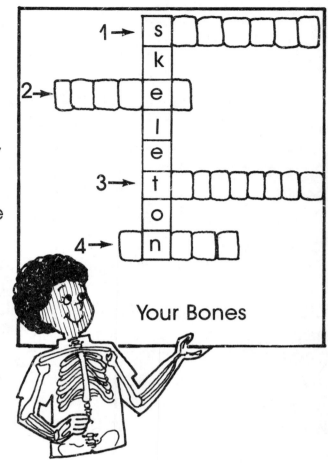

Your Bones

Write.

All the bones in your body form a _____.

muscle   skeleton

Check.

Your skeleton ☐ is made of skin and hair.

☐ supports and holds your body together.

Write.

Your body has _____ bones.

How many?

Unscramble and write in puzzle.

3 → The _____ is the largest bone in your body.

o h g n t i b h e
7 2 4 8 1 3 6 5 9

The smallest bones in your body are called:

2 → _____   4 → _____   1 → _____

m h e m a r   v n i l a   r p u s r t i
3 1 5 4 2 6   3 2 4 5 1   4 7 6 1 5 2 3

• Draw a picture of your skeleton. Name as many bones as you can.

Ask About:

A Rainbow

Have you ever seen a rainbow? A rainbow is an arch of beautiful colors. It appears in the sky when the sun shines after a rainshower. You can see a rainbow when the sun is behind you and the sky in front of you is moist from the rain.

Every rainbow has these colors: violet, indigo, blue, green, yellow, orange and red. These colors are always in the sunlight. When the sunlight shines on the raindrops, the colors separate. Each color can be seen!

You can make a rainbow by turning on a garden hose with the sun behind you. Try it!

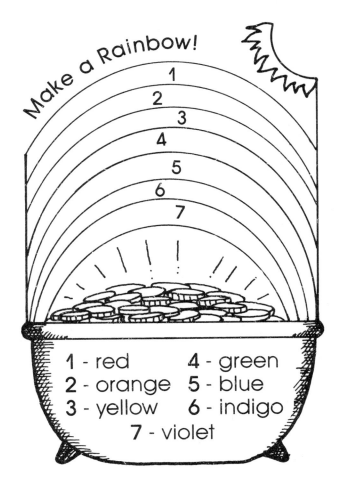

Make a Rainbow!

1 - red   4 - green
2 - orange 5 - blue
3 - yellow 6 - indigo
     7 - violet

Circle.

A   crayon   is an arch of beautiful colors.
      rainbow

Underline.

When can you see a rainbow?
    When the sun and rain are in front of you
    When the sun is behind you and the moist air is in front of you

Write.

Name the colors of the rainbow.

r _____   o _____   y _____

g _____   b _____   i _____   v _____

Check. ☐ These colors are always in the sunlight.
          ☐ Only children can see rainbows.
          ☐ When the sun shines on raindrops, the colors separate.

• Draw and color a rainbow.

7

Ask About:

Clouds

Do you like to watch clouds float by? Do you know how they are made?

The air holds water that the warm sun has pulled, or evaporated, from the earth. When this water cools in the air, it forms clouds. Clouds hold this water until they become full. Then, the water falls to the earth as rain or snow.

When a cloud is formed low along the ground, it is called fog.

Clouds are named for the way they look. Cirrus clouds are thin and high in the sky. Stratus clouds are low and thick. Cumulus clouds are white and puffy.

Circle.

The air holds water that the warm sun has   burned.
                                              evaporated.

Write.

When the water _____ in the air, it forms clouds.
              heats   cools

Check.

When clouds are full, the water falls to the earth as:
☐ money   ☐ snow   ☐ rain   ☐ sunshine

Write.

When a cloud is formed low on the ground, it is called _____.
                                                        fog   fall

Write.

A - Cirrus   ◯ White, puffy clouds
B - Stratus   ◯ Thin, high clouds
C - Cumulus   ◯ Low, thick clouds

Write the name of each cloud in the picture.

• Write a poem about clouds.

Ask About:

Lightning

Lightning is a flash of light caused by electricity in the sky. Clouds are made of many water droplets. All of these droplets together contain a large electrical charge. Sometimes these clouds set off a huge spark of electricity called lightning. Lightning travels very fast. As it cuts through the air, it can cause thunder.

Some lightning can look different from other lightning. Some looks like a zigzag in the sky. Sheet lightning spreads and lights the sky. Ball lightning looks like a ball of fire.

Underline.

Lightning is a flash of light   caused by sunshine.
caused by electricity in the sky.

Yes or No

Sometimes clouds set off a huge spark of electricity.   Yes   No
Lightning is caused by dry weather.   Yes   No
Lightning travels very fast.   Yes   No
Lightning can cause thunder.   Yes   No

Unscramble and write in the puzzle above.

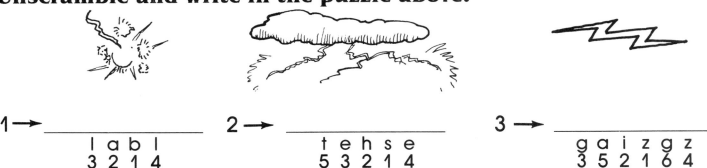

1 → _____
l a b l
3 2 1 4

2 → _____
t e h s e
5 3 2 1 4

3 → _____
g a i z g z
3 5 2 1 6 4

• Draw a picture of a sky with the three kinds of lightning.

Ask About:

Thunder

Have you ever been scared by the sound of thunder? Long, long ago, people believed that thunder was the sound of angry gods in the sky. But now, scientists can tell us exactly what causes thunder.

During an electrical storm, lightning passes through the air. The air is heated by the lightning. This hot air moves out in all directions. As it does, it runs into, or collides, with cooler air. This causes a loud noise, called thunder.

Thunder can have different sounds. A loud crash comes from the main part of lightning. A low rumble means the lightning is farther away.

Check.

☐ Long ago, people believed thunder came from cracks in the earth.

☐ Long ago, people believed thunder was the sound of angry gods.

Write 1-2-3.

◯ The hot air collides with cool air, causing thunder.

◯ Lightning heats the air as it passes through.

◯ The hot air moves out in all directions.

Match.

A loud crash . . .   means the lightning is farther away.

A low rumble . . .   comes from the main part of lightning.

Circle the words that tell how thunder might sound.

• Draw a picture of how people long ago felt when they heard lightning.

Ask About:

A Tornado

Name_____

Did you know that a tornado is the most violent windstorm on Earth? A tornado is a whirling, twisting storm that is shaped like a funnel 🌪 .

A tornado usually occurs in the spring on a hot day. It begins with thunderclouds and thunder. A cloud becomes very dark. The bottom of the cloud begins to twist and form a funnel. Rain and lightning begin. The funnel cloud drops from the dark storm clouds. It moves down toward the ground.

A tornado is very dangerous. It can destroy almost everything in its path.

Circle.

A thunder / tornado   is the most violent windstorm on Earth.

Check.
Which words describe a tornado?
☐ whirling ☐ twisting ☐ icy ☐ funnel-shaped ☐ dangerous

Underline.
A funnel shape is: ◯ ▢ ⬭ ▽ 〰

Write and Circle.

A tornado usually occurs in the _____ on a cool/hot day.
autumn   spring

Write 1-2-3 below and in the picture above.
◯ The funnel cloud drops down to the ground.
◯ A tornado begins with dark thunderclouds.
◯ The dark clouds begin to twist and form a funnel.

• Draw a dark funnel cloud.

Ask About:

A Hurricane

A hurricane is a powerful storm that forms over some parts of an ocean. A hurricane can be several hundred miles wide.

A hurricane has two main parts: the eye and the wall cloud. The eye is the center of the storm. In the eye, the weather is calm. The storm around the eye is called the wall cloud. It has strong winds and heavy rain. In some hurricanes, the wind can blow 150 miles an hour!

As the storm moves across the water, it causes giant waves in the ocean. As the storm moves over land it can cause floods, destroy buildings and kill people who have not taken shelter.

eye

wall clouds

Circle.

A hurricane has two main parts:
    tornado
    wall cloud
    eye

Write.

| wall cloud |
| eye |

_____ The calm center of the hurricane

_____ The wind and rainstorm around the eye

Check:

A hurricane
☐ can be several hundred miles wide.
☐ can have winds that move 150 miles an hour.
☐ is a small storm.
☐ can cause giant waves in the ocean.
☐ can cause floods and hurt people.

• Draw a picture of the eye of a hurricane.

Ask About:

A Volcano

Have you ever wondered what makes a volcano? It starts as a crack in the earth. Lava, which is hot liquid rock, comes up through the crack. When the lava comes out, it is called an eruption. When a volcano erupts, it makes a loud noise. The hot glowing lava, steam and ash pour out of the crack. As the lava cools, it gets hard. Over the years, the hard lava builds up and forms a mountain around the crack. Many volcanic mountains have taken thousands of years to form! Volcanoes do not erupt all the time. Some go for years without erupting. Some volcanoes stop erupting forever. They are called extinct.

Write.

A _____ starts as a crack in the earth.
   rock   volcano

Check.
What is lava?
   Dust
   Hot, liquid rock

Write 1-2-3-4.
How does a volcano form?
   ⃝ Over the years, the hard lava forms a mountain.
   ⃝ A volcano starts as a crack in the earth.
   ⃝ The lava cools and gets hard.
   ⃝ Lava, steam and ash pour out of the crack.

Write.

| A. extinct |
| B. eruption |

_____ Lava coming out of a volcano
_____ A volcano that has stopped erupting

• Draw an erupting volcano. Color the lava red.

Name_____

Icebergs

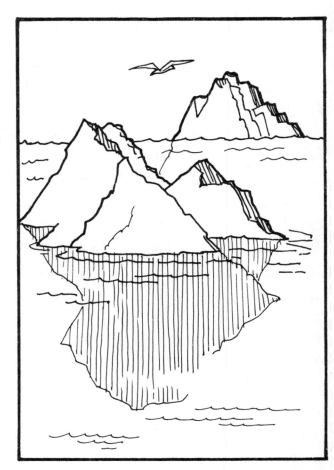

You probably know that icebergs are huge masses of ice that are floating in parts of the oceans. But, do you know where icebergs come from?

Icebergs begin as part of ice on land, called glaciers. As the glaciers move, chunks of ice break off and fall into the ocean. These huge chunks are called icebergs.

As an iceberg floats in the water, the sun melts its top. The part under-water does not melt so quickly. So an iceberg may look small on top of the water, but still be huge underneath. This can be very dangerous for ships. The iceberg underwater can tear open a ship which passes too close!

Write.

An _____ is a huge mass of ice floating in the ocean.
　　island　　iceberg

Circle.

Icebergs were once part of:　valleys　glaciers　floats

Yes or No

As an iceberg floats in the water, the sun melts its top.　　Yes　No
The iceberg underwater does not melt as quickly.　　Yes　No
An iceberg is ice on land.　　Yes　No

Underline.

Which part of the iceberg is larger?
　　The part above the water
　　The part under the water

Draw a ship passing closely to the iceberg in the ocean.

• Draw an iceberg breaking off from a glacier into the ocean.

Ask About:

Fables

A fable is a story that teaches a lesson. Most fables are short stories about animals. The animals think and talk like people. The lesson from the story is called the moral.

The most famous fables were written by Aesop hundreds of years ago. One of his fables told of a fox who tried to reach for grapes hanging on a vine above his head. He tried and tried, but he could not reach them. As he angrily went away, he said that the grapes were probably sour anyway. The moral was. . .a person sometimes pretends that he does not want something he cannot have!

Write.

A _____ is a story that teaches a lesson.
   mystery   fable

Check.

The lesson from a fable is called a

- ☐ duty.
- ☐ moral.
- ☐ lesson.

Unscramble.

_____ wrote the most famous fables.

```
e  A  p  o  s
2  1  5  4  3
```

Write 1-2-3 in the O's below and in the picture above.

⟡ The fox could not reach the grapes.

⟡ The fox tried to reach the grapes.

⟡ The fox said the grapes were probably sour anyway.

• Write your own fable.

    15

Ask About:

Myths

Long ago, people did not understand why many things happened. They did not know why it rained, what caused lightning or how things grew. They made up stories about gods and goddesses who had special powers to make these things happen. These stories are called myths. Many of these gods and goddesses were thought to look like people. Others were thought to look like animals. Many of the gods and goddesses were said to live on mountaintops or in the sky.

People today still like to read myths from long ago. They tell how people long ago felt about the world around them.

Circle.

Long ago, people did not understand   where the Earth was.
    why things happened.

Check.

They made up stories about
☐ gods.
☐ friends who had special powers.
☐ goddesses.

Write.

The gods and goddesses were thought to look like:

_____ or _____.
  party   people   lightning   animals

Circle.

Where did the gods and goddesses live?

mountain tops   hotel   sky

• Write a myth about why it snows.

Ask About:
A Unicorn

A unicorn is a mythical creature. It was said to look much like a horse, except for a large twirly horn on its forehead. The name unicorn means one horn. The unicorn stands for purity and strength. It was described as having blue eyes and a white body.

It was believed that a unicorn was pure and magical. It was thought that if a unicorn dipped its horn into a sea of poison, the water would become clear.

Everyone wanted to possess the magical horn of a unicorn. Legends say that young girls would lead unicorns to kings who would cut off the horns to gain their magical powers.

Check.

Unicorn means ☐ one horse. ☐ one horn.

Yes or No

A unicorn stands for purity and strength.	Yes	No
A unicorn works for kings.	Yes	No
A unicorn's horn was thought to be magical.	Yes	No

Write.

Young girls would lead unicorns to _____.
water   kings

The kings would cut off the horns to gain _____ powers.
magical   poison

Colors: **unicorn** - white **eyes** - blue

• Write a poem about a unicorn.

Ask About:

Dragons

Do you believe that dragons are real? Dragons are mythical creatures. Many countries have legends about dragons. The legends describe dragons as large lizardlike beasts that breathe fire. Most legends speak of dragons as dangerous beasts that lived in dark caves. The legends say that the dragons guarded riches found in these caves. Anyone who killed a dragon would receive the riches. These legends tell of men who killed, or slew, dragons and became heroes.

Some countries have legends about friendly dragons who stand for good luck and riches.

Check.

A dragon was said to be

☐ a lizardlike beast.
☐ a fire-breathing beast.
☐ a shy, quiet lizard.

Write.

Most legends describe dragons as _____ beasts.
　　　　　　　　　　　　　　　dangerous　　lucky

The dragons were said to guard _____ full of riches.
　　　　　　　　　　　　　　cottages　　caves

Men who _____ the dragons would receive the riches.
　　　　slew　　caught

Circle.

In some countries, dragons stand for

good luck.
bad weather.
riches.

Color: **dragon** - green　　**fire** - red

• Draw a dragon guarding its cave full of riches.

Ask About:

A Centaur

A centaur is a mythical creature that was believed to be half horse and half man.

Stories of centaurs are found in myths from the country of Greece. Centaurs were thought to be cruel, wild creatures. They attacked people and animals.

But the most famous centaur, named Chiron, was not like the others. He was wise and gentle. He taught many Greek heroes about music, medicine and hunting. When he died, he became a constellation of stars in the sky. The constellation is called Sagittarius.

Write and Circle.

A _____ was said to be
   centaur   century

half man.
half cat.
half horse.

Unscramble.

The myth of the centaur comes from the country of _____.

r e G c e e
2 3 1 5 4 6

Check.

Centaurs were thought to be   ☐ cruel.   ☐ sleepy.   ☐ wild.

Yes or No

The most famous centaur was Chiron.	Yes	No
Chiron was wise and gentle.	Yes	No
Chiron taught Greek heroes many things.	Yes	No
Chiron was cruel and wild.	Yes	No

Draw a line to connect the stars to make Sagittarius.

• Write a story about Chiron.

Ask About:

Minotaur

The Minotaur was a ferocious, mythical beast that lived on the island of Crete. It was said to have the body of a man and the head of a bull.

The legend tells that the Minotaur was locked up in a great maze under the palace of the wicked King Minos. The king would send people into the maze for the Minotaur to kill.

Theseus, the son of a good king, fell in love with King Minos' daughter. He went into the maze and killed the evil Minotaur. He found his way out of the maze by following a trail of woolen string he had unrolled on his way into the maze!

Unscramble.

The _____ was a mythical beast on the island of Crete.

```
t i o M n r u a
5 2 4 1 3 8 7 6
```

Match.

The Minotaur had the: body of a   bull
                        head of a   man

Write.

King Minos kept the Minotaur in a _____.

                        palace   maze

Check.

☐ Theseus fell in love with the daughter of King Minos.
☐ The Minotaur killed King Minos.
☐ Theseus killed the Minotaur.
☐ Theseus followed a trail of string to get out of the maze.

Draw a line through the maze from Theseus to the Minotaur.

• Make up your own maze.

Ask About:

Mermaids

Do you believe in mermaids? A mermaid is a mythical creature. Through the years people have written about a sea creature which is said to be half woman and half fish. Mermaids are described as having long, golden hair and beautiful singing voices.

Mermaids are said to sit on rocks and comb their long hair. When they see a man, they put a cap on his head. The cap is thought to be magic. It allows the person wearing it to live underwater with the mermaid.

If you swim in the ocean, perhaps **you** will see a mermaid!

Write.

A mermaid is a _____ creature.
desert   mythical

Check.

What is a mermaid said to look like?

☐ half woman   ☐ half fish   ☐ 4 legs   ☐ long, golden hair

Circle.

I sit on a   step / rock   and comb my   voice. / hair.

I have a beautiful   singing / swimming   voice.

I have a   magical / mirror   cap that I put on a man.

Draw a mermaid in the water.

• Write a story about meeting a mermaid.

Ask About:

The Abominable Snowman

The abominable snowman is a creature that some people believe lives on the highest mountain in the world, Mount Everest.

The abominable snowman is called Yeti. It is thought to be a huge, hairy animal with a body like an ape and a head much like a human. It is believed that Yeti comes down from the mountain and attacks the people and animals in the villages.

Some people believe that is is just a bear or gorilla. Others believe that high in the mountains is a real Yeti! What do you think?

Yes or No

Some people believe that an abominable snowman really exists.	Yes	No
They believe the snowman lives on Mount Everest.	Yes	No
They believe the snowman is made of snow and ice.	Yes	No
Mount Everest is the highest mountain in the world.	Yes	No

Unscramble.

The abominable snowman is called _____.

e i Y t
2 4 1 3

Match.

Yeti is thought to have a:

    hairy body   . . . much like a human.
    head   . . . like an ape.

Color Yeti brown.

• Draw a picture of where you think Yeti would live in the mountains.

Ask About:

Name_____

The Loch Ness Monster

Do you know about one of the most famous monsters in the world? It is the Loch Ness Monster. It is a large animal that some people believe lives in Loch Ness, a deep dark lake in Scotland. For many years, hundreds of people have reported seeing something strange in the lake. They have even given it a nickname— "Nessie"!

Nessie is said to be about 30 feet long, with a long slender neck, one or two humps and flippers.

There are even pictures which have been taken of a large animal-like shape in the water. Scientists are still trying to solve the mystery of Nessie!

Circle and Write in Puzzle.

1 → Where is the Loch Ness Lake?
Scotland   Highland

2 → It is famous for the Loch Ness . . .
people   Monster

3 → What is the monster's nickname?
Nellie   Nessie

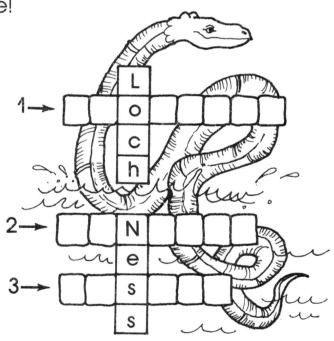

Check.
How has Nessie been described?

☐ about 30 feet long   ☐ 8 legs
☐ long neck   ☐ 1 or 2 humps

Write.
Hundreds of people have _____ seeing Nessie.

studied   reported

Draw a picture of how you think Nessie would look under the water.

• Write a story of how you would look for Nessie!

Ask About:

Atlantis

Have you ever heard of the lost continent of Atlantis? Legend says that Atlantis was a great island in the Atlantic Ocean. Earthquakes and floods shook Atlantis and sank it.

Over the years, countries have sent ships sailing the ocean looking for Atlantis.

The story of Atlantis was first told by a famous Greek named Plato. Later, his tale fascinated many people. Explorers sailing the ocean thought they had found Atlantis many times. They were really finding the many islands that lie in the Atlantic Ocean.

Unscramble and Circle.

Legend says that _____ was an island in the   Pacific   Ocean.
                          t n i A a l s t   Atlantic
                          2 5 7 1 4 3 8 6

Write.

_____ and _____ shook and sank Atlantis.
Tornadoes   Earthquakes   snow   floods

Check.

The story of Atlantis was first told by   explorers.
                                         Plato.

Yes or No

Countries have sent ships looking for Atlantis.	Yes	No
Some explorers thought they had found Atlantis.	Yes	No
Atlantis is a nice vacation island.	Yes	No
Explorers were finding other islands in the Atlantic Ocean.	Yes	No

• Draw a picture of how you believe Atlantis would have looked.

Ask About:

Pompeii

Almost 2000 years ago, Pompeii was a rich and beautiful city in the Bay of Naples. The city lay close to a great volcano Mount Vesuvius.

One day, Vesuvius began to rumble and erupt. Lava, steam and ash burst from the volcano. Soon the sky was black with ash. The ash rained down on Pompeii. The people tried to hide in buildings or escape to the sea in boats. But, the ash fell so quickly that people were buried wherever they were. The city was covered with over twelve feet of ash!

In recent years, scientists have found Pompeii. Much of its contents were just as they were the day Mount Vesuvius erupted.

Unscramble.

_____ was once a city in the Bay of Naples.

```
o e i P m p i
2 5 6 1 3 4 7
```

Circle.

Pompeii lay close to   Mount Everest,   a great volcano.
                        Mount Vesuvius,

Write 1-2-3-4.

What happened when Vesuvius erupted?

- ◯ People tried to hide or escape in boats.
- ◯ Mount Vesuvius began to rumble and erupt.
- ◯ The city was buried in the ash.
- ◯ Ash began raining down on the city.

• Draw a picture of how you think Pompeii looked when it was found.

Ask About:

A UFO

Have you ever seen a UFO? A UFO is an **U**nidentified **F**lying **O**bject. A UFO is a strange object or light that people see in the sky. Many people believe that these strange lights are really spaceships from another planet.

For years, people have seen and heard many odd things in the sky: blinking and glowing lights, flying objects shaped like saucers and moving objects making strange noises. Some people have even taken pictures of these unusual sights.

Some of these UFO's are really airplanes, weather balloons or meteors. But, many UFO reports are still a mystery!

Write (see story).
What does UFO stand for?

U _____   F _____   O _____

Circle.

Many people believe these UFO's are   airplanes
                                        spaceships   from other planets.

Check.
What odd things have people reported seeing or hearing?

☐ Blinking and glowing lights
☐ Saucer-shaped flying objects
☐ Large, red parachutes
☐ Moving objects making strange noises.

Circle.
Some UFO's are really:

airplanes   weather balloons   kites   meteors

• Write a story about a UFO.

Ask About:

The Solar System

Our solar system is made up of the sun and all the objects that go around, or orbit, the sun.

The sun is the only star in our solar system. It gives heat and light to the nine planets in the solar system. The planets and their moons all orbit the sun.

The time it takes for each planet to orbit the sun is called a year. A year on Earth is 365 days. Planets closer to the sun have shorter years. Their orbit is shorter. Planets farther from the sun take longer to orbit, so their years are longer. A year on Pluto is 248 of our years!

Asteroids, comets and meteors are also part of our solar system.

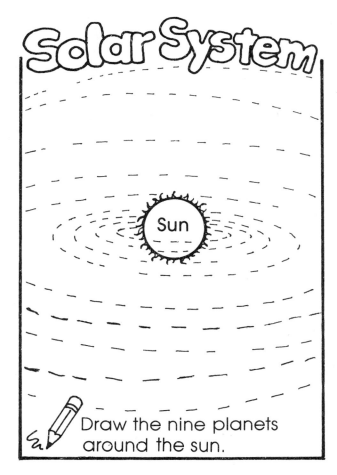

Draw the nine planets around the sun.

Underline.

The solar system is: the sun without the nine planets.
the sun and all the objects that orbit the sun.

Check.

☐ is the center of our solar system.
☐ is the only star in our solar system.
☐ is a planet in our solar system.
☐ gives heat and light to our solar system.

Write.

A _____ is the time it takes for a planet to orbit the sun.
　month　　year

Match.

Planets closer to the sun . . .　　　　have a longer year.
Planets farther from the sun . . .　　have a shorter year.

• Draw and color a picture of our solar system.

Ask About:

Mercury

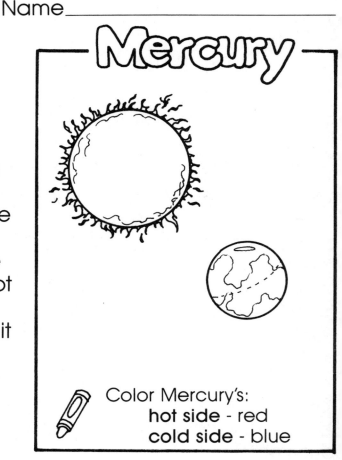

Mercury is one of the smallest of the nine planets in our solar system. It is also the nearest planet to the sun.

Mercury spins very slowly. The side next to the sun gets very hot before it turns away from the sun. The other side freezes while away from the sun. As the planet slowly spins, the frozen side then becomes burning hot and the hot side becomes freezing cold.

Even though Mercury spins slowly, it moves around the sun very quickly. That is why it was named Mercury— after the Roman messenger for the gods.

Color Mercury's:
hot side - red
cold side - blue

Underline.

Mercury   is the largest planet in our solar system.
           is the smallest planet in our solar system.

Write.

Mercury is the _____ planet to the sun.
              darkest   nearest

Match.

How does spinning slowly affect the temperature on Mercury?

The side next to the sun   is freezing cold.

The side away from the sun   is burning hot.

Circle.

Mercury moves   quickly   around the sun.   Mercury spins very   lightly.
                quietly   slowly.

Check.

Mercury was named for the   ☐ famous Roman speaker.
                            ☐ Roman messenger for the gods.

• Find out more about Mercury, the Roman messenger for the gods.

Ask About:

Venus

Venus is the nearest planet to Earth. Because it is the easiest planet to see in the sky, it has been called the Morning Star and Evening Star. The Romans named Venus after their goddess of love and beauty.

Venus is covered with thick clouds. The sun's heat is trapped by the clouds. The temperature on Venus is nearly 900 degrees!

Space probes have been sent to study Venus. They have reported information to scientists. But they can only last a few hours on Venus because of the high temperature.

Venus turns in the opposite direction from Earth. So, on Venus, the sun rises in the west and sets in the east!

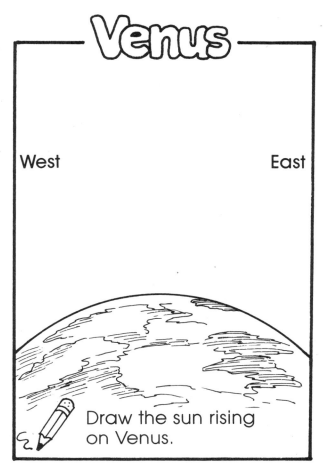

West   East

Draw the sun rising on Venus.

Unscramble and Circle.

_____ is the friendliest planet to Earth.
    e s V u n   nearest
    2 5 1 4 3

Check.

It is called the
☐ Evening Sun
☐ Morning Star   because it is so easy to see.
☐ Evening Star

Circle.

The Romans named Venus for their:

goddess of love and beauty   god of light   goddess of truth

Yes or No

Half of Venus is frozen with ice and snow.   Yes   No
Space probes have reported information from Venus.   Yes   No
On Venus, the sun rises in the east and sets in the west.   Yes   No

• Draw a picture of what a space probe would see on Venus.

Ask About:

Mars

Mars is often called the Red Planet because it looks like a red star in the night sky.

Mars is the fourth planet from the sun. It is only half the size of Earth. But since it has no oceans or lakes, it has as much land as Earth. There is no rainfall on Mars. The planet has many large deserts with huge dust storms that cover the entire planet.

Mars has seasons much like Earth's, but they last twice as long. Mars has two small moons.

Robot spacecraft have landed on Mars. They have sent back thousands of pictures. These pictures show volcanoes, canyons and channels on Mars. But, so far, they show no signs of life on Mars.

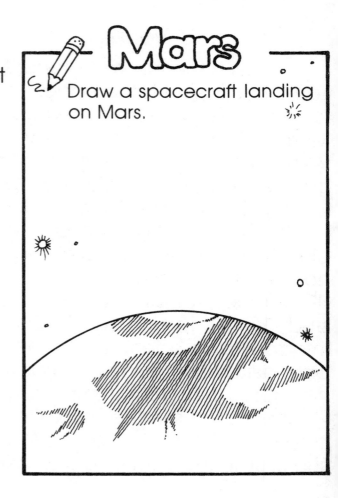

Mars

Draw a spacecraft landing on Mars.

Check.

☐ Mars looks like a red star in the night sky.
☐ Mars is the fourth planet from the sun.
☐ Mars is twice the size of Earth.
☐ Mars has two small moons.
☐ Mars has longer seasons than Earth.

Unscramble.

Mars is often called the _____   _____.

```
e R d          e n P t a l
2 1 3          5 4 1 6 3 2
```

Circle.

What would you find on Mars?

rain   ocean   canyon   channel   lake   volcano   dust

• Write a story about what you would like to find on Mars.

Ask About:

Name_____

Jupiter

Jupiter is the largest planet in our solar system. It has sixteen moons. Jupiter is the second brightest planet— only Venus is brighter.

Jupiter is bigger and heavier than all of the other planets together. It is covered with thick clouds. Many loose rocks and dust particles form a ring around Jupiter.

One of the most fascinating things about Jupiter is its Great Red Spot. The Great Red Spot of Jupiter is a huge storm in the atmosphere. It looks like a red ball. This giant storm is larger than Earth! Every six days it goes completely around Jupiter.

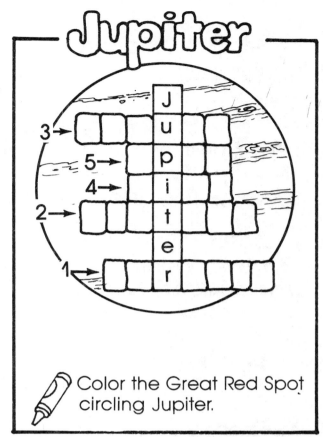

Color the Great Red Spot circling Jupiter.

Unscramble and write in puzzle.

1 → Jupiter is the _____ planet in our solar system.   2 → Jupiter
　　　　　　　　　　　e t s l r g a
　　　　　　　　　　　5 7 6 1 3 4 2

has _____ moons.   3 → Jupiter is covered with thick
　　　t n x s e i e
　　　4 7 3 1 5 2 6

_____.   4 → Loose rocks and dust form a _____ around
d s o c l u　　　　　　　　　　　　　　　　　　　　　g i r n
5 6 3 1 2 4　　　　　　　　　　　　　　　　　　　　　4 2 1 3

Jupiter.   5 → The Great Red _____ of Jupiter is a huge storm.
　　　　　　　　　　　　　　　　t S o p
　　　　　　　　　　　　　　　　4 1 3 2

Circle and Write.

Jupiter is the second   largest   planet.
　　　　　　　　　　　　brightest

Jupiter is _____ and   lighter   than all planets together.
　　　　　bigger   redder   heavier

• Draw Jupiter, its sixteen moons and the Great Red Spot.

31

Ask About:

Saturn

Saturn is probably most famous for its rings. The rings which circle Saturn are made of billions of tiny pieces of ice and dust. Although these rings are very wide, they are very thin. If you look at the rings from the side, they are almost too thin to be seen.

Saturn is the second largest planet in our solar system. It is so big that 758 Earths could fit inside it!

Saturn is covered by clouds. Strong, fast winds move the clouds quickly across the planet.

Saturn has 22 moons! Its largest moon is called Titan.

Saturn

Draw 22 moons around Saturn!

Circle.

Saturn is most famous for its   spots.      rings.

Write.

Saturn's rings are made of _____ and _____.
                              mud   ice   dust   moons

Check.

Saturn's rings are   ☐ red, yellow and purple.
                      ☐ wide, but thin.

Underline.

Saturn ooo is the second largest planet in our solar system.
is big enough to hold 758 Earths inside it.
is farther from the sun than any other planet.
is covered by fast, strong winds.
has 22 moons.

Unscramble.

Saturn's largest moon is called _____.

i T a n t
2 1 4 5 3

• Color Saturn's rings blue.

Ask About:

Uranus

Did you know that Uranus was first thought to be a comet? Many scientists studied the mystery "comet." It was soon decided that Uranus was a planet. It was the first planet to be discovered through a telescope.

Scientists believe that Uranus is made of rock and metal with gas and ice surrounding it.

Even through a telescope, Uranus is not easy to see. That is because it is almost two billion miles from the sun that lights it. It takes Uranus 84 Earth years to orbit the sun!

Scientists know that Uranus has five moons and is circled by nine thin rings. But there are still many mysteries about this faraway planet.

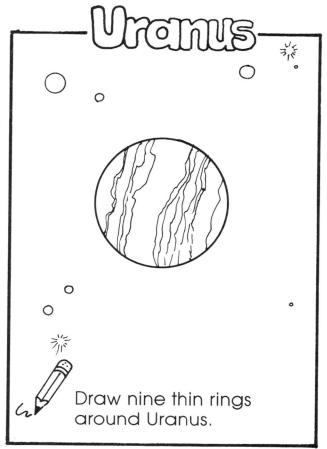

Draw nine thin rings around Uranus.

Circle.

Uranus was first thought to be a   moon.
                                           comet.

Write.

Uranus was the first planet to be discovered through a _____.
                                                         telescope   TV

Check.

Scientists believe that Uranus is made of:

☐ rock   ☐ oil   ☐ metal   ☐ oceans   ☐ gas   ☐ ice

Match.

two billion miles   . . .the number of Uranus' moons

84 Earth years   . . .the distance of Uranus from the sun

five   . . .the number of Uranus' rings

nine   . . .the time it takes Uranus to orbit the sun

• Draw a telescope that could be used to view Uranus.

Ask About:

Neptune

Neptune is the eighth planet from the sun. It is difficult to see Neptune— even through a telescope. It is almost three billion miles from Earth.

Scientists believe that Neptune is much like Uranus—made of rock, iron, ice and gases.

Neptune has two moons. Scientists believe that it may also have rings.

Neptune is so far away from the sun that it takes 164 Earth years for it to orbit the sun just once!

Neptune is a cold and distant planet that scientists still know very little about.

Write, Circle or Unscramble.

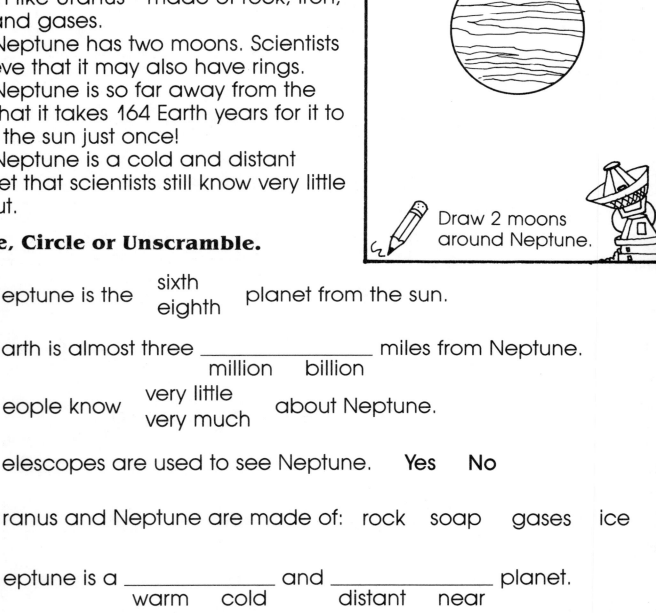

Neptune

Draw 2 moons around Neptune.

N eptune is the   sixth / eighth   planet from the sun.

E arth is almost three _____ miles from Neptune.
million   billion

P eople know   very little / very much   about Neptune.

T elescopes are used to see Neptune.   **Yes   No**

U ranus and Neptune are made of: rock   soap   gases   ice

N eptune is a _____ and _____ planet.
warm   cold   distant   near

E very orbit around the _____ takes Neptune 164 Earth years.
u s n
2 1 3

• Find out how Neptune got its name.

Ask About:

Pluto

Pluto is the ninth planet from the sun. It is farther from the sun than any other planet.

If you stood on Pluto, the sun would look just like a bright star in the sky. Pluto is so far away that it gets little of the sun's heat. That is why it is freezing cold on Pluto.

Some scientists think that Pluto was once one of Neptune's moons that escaped from orbit and drifted into space. Other scientists believe it has always been a planet in our solar system.

Pluto is so far away from the sun that it takes 247 Earth years just to orbit the sun once!

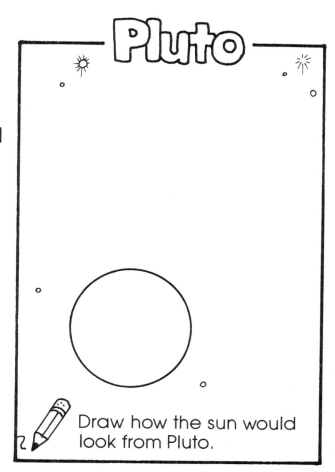

Draw how the sun would look from Pluto.

Unscramble and Circle.

_____ is the   seventh
   l t P o u   ninth   planet from the sun.
   2 4 1 5 3

Pluto is   closest
        farther   from the _____ than any other planet.
                        n u s
                        3 2 1

Check.

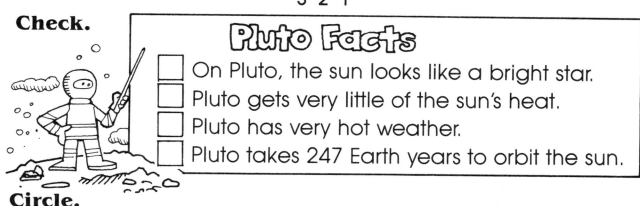

Pluto Facts

- ☐ On Pluto, the sun looks like a bright star.
- ☐ Pluto gets very little of the sun's heat.
- ☐ Pluto has very hot weather.
- ☐ Pluto takes 247 Earth years to orbit the sun.

Circle.

Some scientists believe that Pluto was once Neptune's   sun.
                                                         moon.

- Write a story about what you would find on Pluto.

Ask About:

Constellations

Name_____

On a clear night, you can see about two thousand stars in the sky. Scientists can use giant telescopes to see billions of stars.

Stars in groups form pictures called constellations. These constellations have been recognized for years. Ancient people named many constellations for animals, heroes and mythical creatures. Many of these names are still used.

Some constellations can be seen every night of the year. Others change with the seasons.

Since all stars are constantly moving, these same constellations that we now see will be changed thousands of years from now.

Connect the stars to form the constellation called the Little Dipper.

Write.

Stars in groups form pictures called _____.

telescopes   constellations

Check.

Ancient people named many constellations for:

☐ animals   ☐ heroes   ☐ oceans   ☐ mythical creatures

Match.

Billions of stars can be seen.

About two thousand stars can be seen.

Yes or No

Some constellations can be seen every night.   Yes   No

Some constellations change with the seasons.   Yes   No

In thousands of years, all constellations will be the same.   Yes   No

• Design your own constellation. Give it a name, too.

Ask About:

The North Star

The North Star is one of the most famous stars. Its star name is Polaris. It is called the North Star because it shines almost directly over the North Pole.

Because the North Star is always in the same spot in the sky, it has been used for years to give direction to people at night.

If you are at the North Pole, the North Star is directly overhead. As you travel south, the star seems lower in the sky. Only people in the Northern Hemisphere can see the North Star.

Polaris, like all stars, is always moving. Thousands of years from now, another star will get to be the North Star.

Write.

The _____ Star is one of the most famous stars.
    Pole   North

Unscramble.

_____ is the star name for the North Star.

a	i	o	l	r	P	s
4	6	2	3	5	1	7

Check.

☆ The North Star is almost directly over the North Pole.

☆ The North Star can be seen from anywhere in the world.

☆ The North Star can help give direction at night.

☆ Only people in the Northern Hemisphere can see the North Star.

☆ Polaris will always be the North Star.

Write the star name for the North Star on the line above.

• Draw a picture showing how the North Star helped sailors years ago.

Ask About:

The Big Dipper

One of the most famous star patterns, or constellations, is called the Big Dipper. It is formed by seven bright stars. Three stars form the handle and four stars form the bowl. The two stars that form the outer part of the bowl always point to the North Star.

The Big Dipper is more than a picture made of stars. It can be used to tell time. That is because as the Earth moves, the Big Dipper appears to turn around the North Star once every 24 hours.

All of the stars in the Big Dipper are constantly moving. Scientists say that in several thousand years, the stars will no longer form the Big Dipper!

Big Dipper

North Star

Connect the dots to form the Big Dipper.

Circle.

One of the most famous constellations is called the:

space probe   Big Dipper   North Star

Check.

The Big Dipper is formed by ☐ four / ☐ seven bright stars.

Match 1-2-3.

Three stars   form the **bowl**.

Four stars   form the **handle**.

Yes or No

Two stars in the Big Dipper point to the North Star.   Yes   No

The Big Dipper catches comets and meteors.   Yes   No

The Big Dipper will **always** look the same.   Yes   No

• Draw a picture of the Big Dipper.

Ask About:

Comets

For many years, people were frightened when a comet appeared in the sky. Now we know that comets are part of our solar system. They move in an orbit around the sun.

A comet looks like a ball of fire with a long tail. When its orbit brings it closer to the sun, its tail gets much longer. This is caused by the wind and heat from the sun. Then, a comet can be 100 million miles long.

Each year new comets are discovered. Some comets can be predicted to reappear at certain times.

One of the most famous comets, Halley's Comet, reappears about once every 76 years!

Unscramble.

_____ are part of our solar system.

```
o  t  s  C  m  e
2  5  6  1  3  4
```

Write.

A comet looks like a ball of _____ with a long _____.
                          ice   fire   tail   tide

Circle and write in puzzle.

1→ A comet moves in an shadow / orbit around the sun.

2→ As a comet gets closer to the sun, its top / tail gets much longer.

3→ One of the most famous comets is named Earth's Comet. / Halley's Comet.

• Draw a comet orbiting the sun. Name your comet.

 Ask About:

A Solar Eclipse

Have you ever seen an eclipse of the sun? It is called a solar eclipse, because solar means sun. A solar eclipse happens when the sun's light is blocked from the Earth. Do you know why this happens?

The moon travels around the Earth. The Earth and the moon travel around the sun. Sometimes, the moon passes exactly between the sun and the Earth. The sun's light is blocked by the moon. The Earth becomes dark. This darkness can last from two to seven minutes. Then, as the moon moves, the sunlight appears again. A solar eclipse is an amazing event!

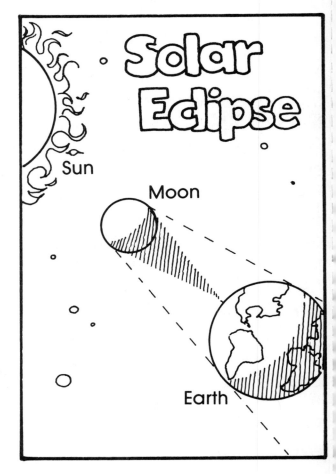

Check.

A solar eclipse happens . . .

☐ when the sun sets in the east.

☐ when the sun's light is blocked from the Earth.

Circle.

The word **solar** means: moon   Earth   sun

Write.

The Earth and _____ travel around the sun.

sun   moon

Underline.

What causes a solar eclipse?

The moon passes between the Earth and sun and blocks the sunlight.

The Earth does not move around the sun.

Color: **Earth** - blue   **moon** - yellow   **sun** - orange

• Draw a picture of the Earth during a solar eclipse.

Ask About:

Name_____

A Black Hole

Have you ever heard of a mysterious black hole? Some scientists believe that a black hole is an invisible object somewhere in space. The scientists believe that it has such a strong pull toward it, called gravity, that nothing can escape from it!

These scientists believe that a black hole is a star that collapsed. The collapse made its pull even stronger. It seems invisible because even its own starlight cannot escape! It is believed that anything in space that comes near the black hole will be pulled into it forever. Some scientists believe there are many black holes in our galaxy.

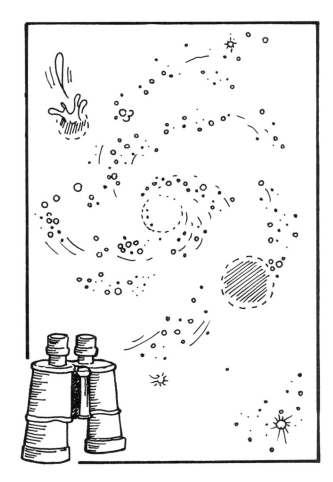

Check.

Some scientists believe that:

- [ ] a black hole is an invisible object in space.
- [ ] a black hole is a collapsed star.
- [ ] a black hole is a path to the other side of the Earth.
- [ ] a black hole has a very strong pull toward it.
- [ ] a black hole will not let its own light escape.

Write.

| A - gravity |
| B - collapse |

_____ To fall or cave in

_____ A strong pull from an object in space

Draw a spaceship being pulled into the black hole.

- Draw what you think the inside of a black hole would be like.

Ask About:

The Midnight Sun

How would you like to live in a land where the sun shines day and night? There are places in the polar regions where, for months, the sun never sets! This is known as the Land of the Midnight Sun. This period of sunlight can last up to six months.

This happens because the Earth tilts. When the North Pole is tilted toward the sun, it has constant daylight. At that same time, the South Pole is tilted away from the sun. It is in darkness.

Six months later, the South Pole tilts to the sun and has constant daylight. Then the North Pole is tilted away. It has darkness.

Midnight

Underline.
In the land of the Midnight Sun,   the sun shines every other day.
                                      the sun shines for months.

Write.

This sunshine can last up to _____ months.
                              ten   six

Circle.
The Midnight Sun happens because the Earth   rests.
                                               tilts.

Write.

> A - constant daylight
> B - constant darkness

_____ The polar region is tilted away from the sun.

_____ The polar region is tilted toward the sun.

Color the Midnight Sun yellow.

• Write a story about life in the Land of the Midnight Sun.

Ask About:

The Milky Way Galaxy

The Milky Way galaxy is made up of the Earth, its solar system and all the stars you can see at night. There are over 100 billion stars in the Milky Way!

The Milky Way is shaped much like a record. It has a center which the outer part goes around.

The Milky Way is always spinning slowly through space. It is so large that it would take 200 million years for the galaxy to turn one complete time.

Many stars in the Milky Way are in clusters. Some star clusters contain up to one million stars!

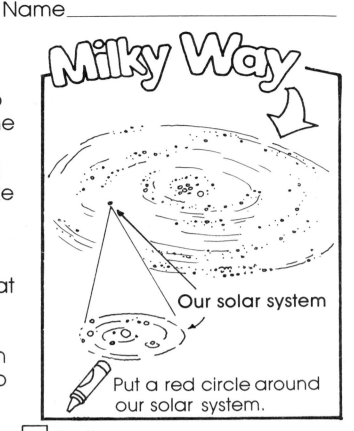

Our solar system

Put a red circle around our solar system.

Check.
The Milky Way galaxy is made up of

☐ Earth.
☐ no sun.
☐ our solar system.
☐ 100 billion stars.

Yes or No

The Milky Way is shaped like a pencil.	Yes	No
The Milky Way is always slowly moving in space.	Yes	No
Many stars in the Milky Way are in clusters.	Yes	No
Some star clusters have one million stars.	Yes	No

Circle.

It would take   200   90   600   million years for the galaxy to spin once.

Underline.
Which object is the Milky Way shaped much like?

 record    ruler

• Write about what the Earth will be like after it circles the Milky Way one time.

Ask About:

A Planetarium

Even though the stars in space are constantly moving, it is hard to see the changes in the sky. It takes thousands of years for some changes to be seen.

A planetarium is a special machine which shows the movements of stars and planets. It does this by placing spots of light on a curved ceiling that stands for the sky. The spots of light are made to appear and move like planets and stars. The machine can be speeded up to show thousands of years of change in just minutes. A planetarium not only can show how the sky will change in the future, but it can also show how the sky appeared thousands of years ago!

Underline.

A planetarium   shows the movements of stars and planets.
                 shows the pictures of rockets.

Write 1-2-3.
How does a planetarium work?

◯ The spots appear and move like planets.

◯ The machine can speed up to show the sky of the future.

◯ The planetarium places spots of light on a curved ceiling.

Check.
Why is a planetarium helpful?

☐ It lets us see how the changes in the sky occur.

☐ It only shows parts of the sky.

• Draw a picture of a planetarium.

Ask About:

Mammals

Did you know that you are a mammal? Mammals are warm-blooded animals. Most mammals have hair on their bodies.

Many mammals live on land. People, elephants, rabbits, dogs and cats are all land mammals.

Some mammals, like dolphins and whales, live in the water.

The seal, walrus and otter are mammals that live on land **and** in the water.

Did you know there is even a mammal that flies? It is the bat!

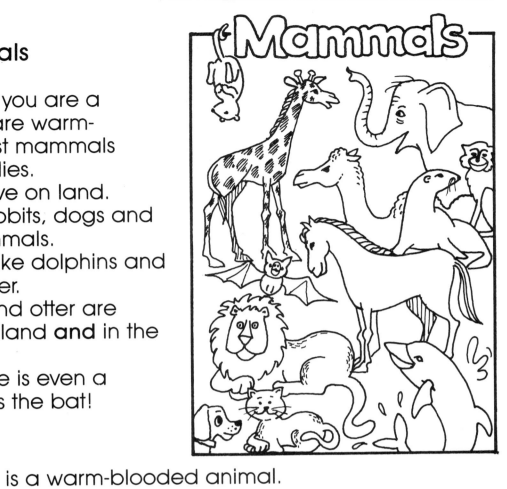

Write.

A _____ is a warm-blooded animal.

    reptile   mammal

Circle.

Most mammals have   hair   on their bodies.

                  scales

Write.

Mammals

cat   dolphin   people   dog   seal   walrus   otter   rabbit   whale   elephant

Land	Water	Land and Water
_____	_____	_____
_____	_____	_____
_____	_____	_____
_____	_____	_____

• Write a list of ten other mammals.

Ask About:

Reptiles

Name_____

Reptiles are a group of animals that are cold-blooded and are usually covered with scales or plates. Because reptiles are cold-blooded, they move around a lot looking for comfortable temperatures. Some reptiles even hibernate.

There are four main groups of reptiles: turtles, lizards, snakes and crocodilians. The crocodilians include alligators.

Most reptiles hatch from eggs. Young reptiles care for themselves.

Although a few snakes and lizards are poisonous, most reptiles are harmless.

Reptiles

Unscramble and Circle.

_____ are
e R p i l e s t
2 1 3 5 6 7 8 4

cold-blooded
warm-blooded   animals.

Write.

Reptiles are usually covered with _____ or _____.

feathers   scales   fur   plates

Circle.

There are   four
            six   main groups of reptiles.

Write on the lines and in the picture above.

| lizards |
| crocodilians |
| turtles |
| snakes |

_____

_____

• Draw a picture of your favorite reptile.

Ask About:

Fossils

Do you ever wonder how scientists know so much about animals and plants that existed long ago? Much of their information comes from studying fossils.

A fossil is any trace found in rocks of living things from the past. Bones, shells and teeth can be fossils.

How are fossils formed? Many dinosaur fossils were formed this way: when some dinosaurs died, their bodies sank into a lake or pond and were gradually covered by mud. In time, the mud hardened into rock. The dinosaur bones inside the rock hardened, too.

People who collect and study fossils are called paleontologists.

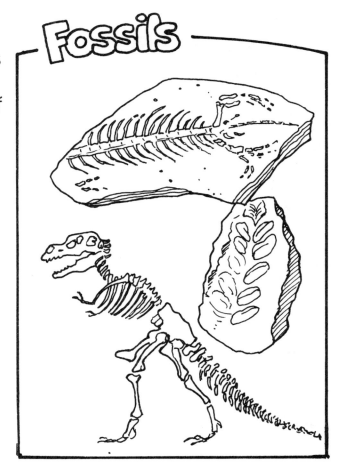

Circle.

Scientists know much about the past from studying   fossils.
                                                     robots.

Underline.

A fossil is   any trace of a living thing found in rocks.
               a scientist's notebook.

Check.

Fossils can be: ☐ bones   ☐ books   ☐ shells   ☐ teeth

Write 1-2-3.

How were some dinosaur fossils formed?

Color the fossil brown.

• Draw a picture of a fossil you would like to find.

Ask About:

The Platypus

The platypus is one of the most unusual animals in the world. The platypus lives along streams in Australia. It is a mammal, even though it lays eggs like a bird.

The platypus has a bill like a duck. That is why it is often called a duckbilled platypus. It uses its bill to hunt for its food in streams. It eats mostly shellfish, worms and insects.

A platypus is about two feet long. It has webbed feet, which makes it an excellent swimmer.

At one time, many platypuses were killed for their fur. It is now against the law to kill a platypus.

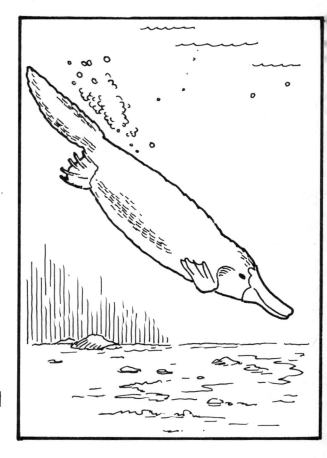

Circle.

The platypus lives along streams in Africa.
Australia.

Yes or No

The platypus is a mammal.	Yes	No
The platypus lays eggs.	Yes	No
The platypus has a bill like a duck.	Yes	No
The platypus is a reptile.	Yes	No

Check.

The platypus eats mostly:

☐ shellfish   ☐ worms   ☐ rabbits   ☐ insects

Circle.

The platypus is an excellent sleeper
swimmer because it has wide
webbed feet.

Underline.

It is against the law to kill a platypus.
to photograph a platypus.

• Write a story about a platypus.

Ask About:

Name_____

A Piranha

The piranha gets its name from an Indian word which means toothfish. A piranha eats mostly other fish. Piranhas are known for attacking their food and stripping it down to the bones in minutes.

Piranhas live in certain South American rivers. They usually swim in groups, or schools, of fifty or sixty. There are about twenty kinds of piranhas. Only four are known to attack large animals. The most vicious is the Black Piranha.

Piranhas will even attack each other. But they have a curious ability to heal quickly from these wounds.

Write and Circle.

Piranha is an ancient
                Indian   word which means _____.
                                          shark   toothfish

Unscramble.

Piranhas live in _____ _____ rivers.
                  S u h t o   m e n A r c a i
                  1 3 5 4 2   2 3 8 1 4 6 7 5

Check.

Piranhas are known for:

☐ attacking their food and stripping it to the bones in minutes.

☐ attacking boats which travel on the river.

Write.

There are about _____ kinds of piranhas.
                 fifty   twenty

Circle.

The most vicious piranha is the   Gold Piranha.
                                   Black Piranha.

• Draw two piranhas attacking each other.

Ask About:

A Komodo Dragon

A Komodo Dragon is not really a dragon. It is the largest living lizard in the world. A Komodo Dragon is at least ten feet long and weighs 360 pounds. It has a long tail and is covered with scales. Its mouth is lined with sharp teeth.

The Komodo Dragon gets its name from the island of Komodo in the Pacific Ocean, where most of these lizards are found. It resembles the giant dragon-like lizards that lived in prehistoric times.

The Komodo dragon hunts food in the day. At night, it hides in caves which it digs with its sharp claws.

Underline.

A Komodo Dragon   is really a dragon.
is really a lizard.

Write in puzzle.

A Komodo Dragon:

is the largest _____ in the world.
1

is covered with _____.
2

is found on _____ _____.
3   4

Komodo

1→ ☐☐☐☐☐ d
r
2→ ☐☐☐ a ☐☐☐
g
3→ ☐☐ o ☐☐☐
4→ ☐☐☐☐ n

Match.

day   hides in caves

night   hunts for food

these words:

Komodo   lizard
scales   Island

• Draw a Komodo Dragon digging its cave.

The Great Ice Age

Long ago, the Great Ice Age began when the climate of Earth began to cool. As the temperature dropped, giant sheets of ice, called glaciers, moved across the land. As time went on, snow and ice covered many forests and grasslands.

Some plants and animals could not survive the changes in the climate. Other animals moved to warmer land. But some animals were able to adapt —they learned to live with the cold and snowy weather.

Finally, the Earth's temperature began to rise. The ice and snow began to melt. Today, the land at the North and South Poles is a reminder of the Great Ice Age!

Check.
The Great Ice Age

☐ began when Earth's climate became cooler.
☐ began with a volcano eruption.

Write.

Sheets of ice, called _____, moved across the land.
sleet   glaciers

Circle.
Snow and ice covered many   forests   and   islands.
                            caves   grasslands.

Check.
What happened to many animals?
☐ Some animals moved to warmer land.
☐ Some animals adapted to the colder weather.
☐ The colder weather did not bother the animals.
☐ Some animals could not survive the colder weather.

• Write a story about the Great Ice Age.

Ask About:

Hibernation

Have you ever wondered why some animals hibernate? Hibernation is a long sleep that some animals go into for the winter.

Animals get their warmth and energy from food. Some animals cannot find enough food in the winter. They must eat large amounts of food in the fall. Their bodies store this food as fat. Then in winter, they sleep in hibernation. Their bodies live on the stored fat. Since their bodies need much less food during hibernation, they can stay alive without eating new food during the winter.

Some animals that hibernate are: bats, chipmunks, bears, snakes and turtles.

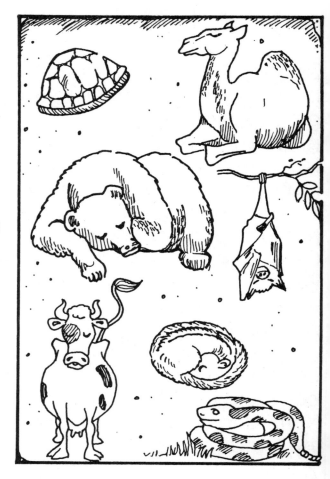

Underline.

Hibernation
    is a sleep that some animals go into for the winter.
    is the time of year to gather food for the winter.

Yes or No.

Animals get their warmth and energy from food.   Yes   No
Some animals cannot find enough food in the winter.   Yes   No
Animals hibernate because they are lazy.   Yes   No
Animals need less food while they are hibernating.   Yes   No

Match.

Animals that hibernate . . .
    eat and store food   in the winter.
    go to sleep   in the fall.

Color the animals that hibernate.

• Draw a bear hibernating in a cave.

Ask About:

Extinction

An animal becomes extinct when every animal of its kind has died.

One of the most famous extinct animals is the dinosaur. Some scientists believe that all of the dinosaurs died because they could not live in a changing climate.

Animals can become extinct for many reasons. Some animals have been hunted and killed. Others have been poisoned by the pollution of the land and water where they live. Some animals become extinct because people now live on the land where they once lived. The animals cannot find new places to live.

Check.
An animal becomes extinct. . .
- ☐ when it moves to a new place to live.
- ☐ when every animal of its kind has died.

Circle.
One of the most famous extinct animals is the   shark.
                                                 dinosaur.

Why do some animals become extinct?

Some animals are _____ and _____.
                  hunted   caged   watched   killed

Some animals are poisoned by   pollution.
                               other animals.

Some animals lose their

_____ and cannot find new ones.
 homes   help

• Find the names of three more extinct animals.

What About:

Velcro

Many things—jackets, wallets, backpacks—have fasteners to open and close them. For years, most things were fastened with zippers, buttons, snaps and buckles. Now, Velcro has become a popular fastener.

Velcro was invented by a Swiss engineer. While camping in the woods, he noticed that burrs would stick to his clothes. Little hooks that covered the burrs would stick to loops of thread on his clothes. He decided to invent a fastener which would work like a burr. He named his product Velcro.

One piece of Velcro is made of tiny hooks—the other piece of tiny loops. When the two pieces come together, they stick. To unfasten—just pull them apart!

hooks

loops

List four fasteners that have been used for years:

1. _____ 2. _____ 3. _____ 4. _____

Circle and Check.

Velvet
Velcro   was invented by   ☐ a Swiss surgeon.
                            ☐ a Swiss engineer.

Write.

Velcro was designed to work like a _____ .

Circle T or F.

Velcro

. . . is used to fasten things.	T	F
. . . is made to work like a zipper.	T	F
. . . is made of tiny hooks and loops.	T	F
. . . has been used as long as buttons have.	T	F

Underline the sentence that tells how to unfasten Velcro.

• List 10 things that could be fastened with Velcro.

What About:

Animal Mysteries

As long as people have studied animals, there have been mysteries about why animals act certain ways.

One mystery has to do with some animals' strange behaviors **before** earthquakes. Horse and cattle stampedes, screeching seabirds, howling dogs, even animals coming out of hibernation early, are examples of this mysterious behavior.

Another mystery involves birds and ants. No one can explain why a bird will pick up an ant in its beak and rub the ant over its feathers again and again. This is called "anting", and birds have been known to do this for an hour without stopping.

One animal mystery is very sad. For hundreds of years, some whales have mysteriously swam from the ocean onto a beach where they would die. Reports of "beached whales" occur about five times a year somewhere in the world.

There are hundreds of other animal mysteries—such as how and why animals hibernate—that scientists have not solved. Can you think of another animal mystery?

3 Animal Mysteries

Write.

1. Some animals act strangely before an_____.

Check.

This strange behavior includes: ☐ laughing birds ☐ howling dogs

☐ horse and cattle stampedes   ☐ barking whales

☐ leaving hibernation early   ☐ screeching seabirds

Write.

2. This mystery is about _____ rubbing _____ over their feathers.

Write.

3. A sad mystery is about _____ swimming onto

a _____ and dying.

• Write a solution to one of the animal mysteries.

What About:

Superstitions

Have you ever avoided walking under a ladder because you thought it would bring you bad luck? If so, you were following a superstition. A superstition is a belief that if you do a certain thing it will cause a totally different thing to happen. Superstitions have existed for hundreds of years. Most people today do not believe old superstitions, but they still follow them just to be safe!

There are superstitions for almost anything people do: sleeping, working, eating, getting married, playing or just walking. There are superstitions about pets, friends, numbers, sports, weather—even the moon.

Some superstitions predict good luck—throwing rice at a bride and groom, knocking on wood, finding a four-leaf clover, or carrying a rabbit's foot. Other superstitions warn of bad luck—spilling salt, breaking a mirror, or having a black cat walk across your path. What do you think of superstitions?

Underline.

A superstition is a belief that . . .

    if you do a certain thing it will cause a totally different thing
      to happen.

    you will always have good luck no matter what you do.

Circle.

Most people   believe / do not believe   in superstitions.

Check.

☐ Superstitions have existed for less than a hundred years.
☐ Superstitions have existed for hundreds of years.

Unscramble.

Superstitions are thought to predict _____ or _____ luck.
                                    d o g o   d b a

Underline six things in the story that superstitions can be about.

• Write a story about superstitions.

What About:

Traveling Seeds

Everyone knows that flowering plants cannot fly or run or walk. But, through their seeds, they move from place to place. That is why you can see new plants growing each year where there were none before.

Flowering plants grow in many different colors and sizes, but they all have seeds. The part of the plant which holds the seeds is called the fruit. Some seeds travel in their fruit. Others fall out and travel to a place where they can grow. But how do they get to this new place?

Some seeds stick to people's clothes or animals' fur and are carried from place to place. The seeds drop off and form new plants where they fall. Other seeds may be scattered by wind and rain. They are blown or washed to a new place where they will grow. Some seeds are not carried by people, animals, wind or rain. They are actually popped out by their own plant to grow nearby.

However it happens, seeds are constantly moving about.

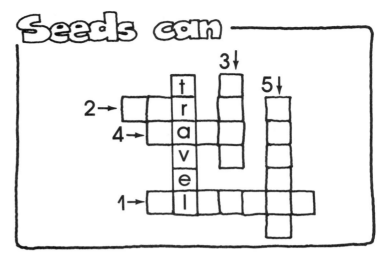

Seeds can

Write.

The part of the plant which holds the seeds is called the _____.

Match.

Some seeds fall from their fruit before they travel.
Some seeds travel in their fruit.

How Do Seeds Travel?

Write and circle.

Some seeds wash / stick to people's _____ or animals' _____ .
                                          1   2

Some seeds are scattered / changed by _____ and _____ .
                                          3   4

Some seeds are _____ out by their own size. / plant.
                    5

Write each word in the puzzle.

• Draw a picture showing the ways seeds can travel.

What About:

Ice Cream

Almost everyone loves to eat ice cream. In fact, ice cream has been a favorite for hundreds of years. Nearly two thousand years ago, Roman rulers enjoyed eating mountain snow. In Europe, people flavored ice for a special dish. In 1295, the great explorer, Marco Polo, brought recipes from China for water ices. Later, cream was used to make ice cream much like we enjoy today.

Until 1851, ice cream was mostly made at home. Today, most ice cream is produced in ice cream plants. These plants use machines to mix milk, sugar and water. The mixture is pumped into a cooler. After it is chilled, it is put into storage tanks. Special flavors and colors are added to make many different kinds of ice cream. The mixtures are then frozen at a temperature of –22°F. Then fan-like blades slice through the frozen mixture and whip air into it. This fluffy ice cream is placed in a hardening room for 12 hours. Then off to the stores it goes!

Name_____

```
1→ [ ][ ][ ][ ][ ][i][ ][ ]
              [c]
2→ [ ][ ][ ][ ][e]
      3→ [ ][ ][ ][c][ ][ ]
              [r]
   4→ [ ][ ][e][ ][ ]
              [a]
      5→ [ ][ ][m][ ]
```

Unscramble, circle, write and check. Write the answers in the puzzle above.

1→ Ice cream has been a _____ treat for many years.
   v t i r f o a e

2→ In England, Europe, people flavored ice for a special dish. 3→ In 1295,

_____ Polo brought recipes from China for water ices.

4→ Later, ☐ ice / ☐ cream was used to make ice cream. 5→ Until 1851,

most ice cream was made at _____ .

Write 1-6. How is ice cream made in plants?

○ After the mixture is chilled, it is put into storage tanks.

○ The different mixtures are frozen at –22°F.

○ Fan-like blades slice through the mixture and whip air into it.

○ A mixture of milk, sugar and water is pumped into a cooler.

○ Special colors and flavors are added.

○ The fluffy ice cream is placed in a hardening room for 12 hours.

What About:

Insects in Winter

In the summertime, insects can be seen buzzing and fluttering around us. But as winter's cold weather begins, suddenly the insects seem to disappear. Do you know where they go?

Many insects, such as flies and mosquitoes, find a warm place to spend the winter. They live in cellars, barns, attics, caves and tree holes.

Beetles and ants try to dig deep into the ground. Some beetles stack up in piles under rocks or dead leaves.

In the fall, female grasshoppers and crickets lay their eggs and die. The eggs

Name_____

hatch in the spring.

Bees also try to protect themselves from the winter cold. Honeybees gather in a ball in the middle of their hive. The bees stay in this tight ball trying to stay warm.

Winter is very hard for insects, but each spring the survivors come out and the buzzing and fluttering begins again.

Write.

When cold weather begins, _____ seem to disappear.

Unscramble and check.

_____ and_____ find a warm place in:

q u t M s o e o s i   s f i l e

☐ beds ☐ barns ☐ caves ☐ cellars ☐ attics ☐ sweaters

Circle Yes or No.

I n the winter, insects look for a warm place to live.   Yes   No

N oise, such as buzzing, can be heard all winter long.   Yes   No

S ome beetles and ants dig deep into the ground.   Yes   No

E very insect finds a warm home for the winter.   Yes   No

C rickets and grasshoppers lay their eggs and die.   Yes   No

T he honeybees gather in a ball! in their hive.   Yes   No

S urvivors of the cold weather come out each spring.   Yes   No

• Draw a picture showing how the insects keep warm in the winter.

What About:

Leap Year

Do you know what leap year is and how it is different from other years? A year is measured on a calendar in months and days. The calendar year has 365 days. That is because it takes the Earth **approximately** 365 days to travel around the sun. Actually, it takes the Earth 365 days, 5 hours, 48 minutes and 45 seconds to make the trip. So every year there are 5 hours, 48 minutes and 45 seconds that we don't use! To solve this problem,

Name_____

every four years this extra time is added up to make an extra day. The year with the extra day is called Leap Year. Leap year has 366 days. The extra day is added to the month of February. The day becomes February 29th.

Circle.

A year is measured on a calendar in   miles   and   days.
                                       months   pounds.

Underline.

It takes the Earth **approximately** 365 days. . .

       to travel around the sun.

       to go from winter to summer.

Write.

Exactly how long does it take the Earth to travel around the sun?

____ days   ____ hours   ____ minutes   ____ seconds

Underline the sentence that tells how much extra time we don't use every year.

Write and check.

Every _____ years the extra time ☐ is added up to make a month.
                                    ☐ is added up to make an extra day.

Write.

The year with the extra day is called _____ Year.

Leap Year has _____ days.

Check.

The extra day becomes ☐ February 2nd. ☐ February 29th.

• Make a calendar page for February during Leap Year.

Reading Comprehension IF8708   60   © 1990 Instructional Fair, Inc.

What About:

Camouflage

A camouflage is a way of disguising or hiding something or someone. Both animals and people use camouflage to protect themselves.

Many animals have a natural camouflage. The color of their skin or fur helps them blend in with their surroundings. This lets them hide from other animals who might harm them. For example, the white polar bear lives on white snow and ice. Its color acts as a camouflage because the white bear is hard to see in all the white surroundings. Brown field mice and green insects have the colors of their natural homes. One animal, the chameleon, can even change colors to match its surroundings as it moves from place to place.

People have learned to use camouflage, too. Soldiers' uniforms are often earth colors so they cannot be easily seen. Warships, tanks and jeeps have been "camouflaged" with colors to match the water or land. Can you think of other camouflages?

Unscramble.

A _____ is a way of disguising something or someone.
u a c o m f l g e a

T or F

animals Natural camouflage does not help animals.   T   F

Many animals have a natural camouflage.   T   F

Check.

Which are examples of natural camouflage?

☐ A white polar bear on white snow and ice

☐ A red bird living in a green tree

☐ A brown field mouse in a brown field

☐ A green insect living in green grass

Underline the animal which can change colors to match its surroundings.

Circle.

What are some examples of camouflage that people have used?

people soldiers' uniforms   tanks   radios   jeeps

• Draw three examples of camouflage for animals and people.

What About:

Hieroglyphic Writing

Can you imagine a time when people were just learning to write symbols for the words they spoke?

Name_____

One of the earliest forms of writing was developed in ancient Egypt. The Egyptians used a kind of picture writing called hieroglyphics.

At first, they used simple pictures to express an idea. These pictures are called pictographs. Later, they used symbols that stood for sounds or parts of words. This picture writing is called syllabic.

Egyptians began by carving their "picture writing" on stone monuments. Later, they learned to make a paper-like material to write on. It was made from a reed plant called papyrus. The Egyptians wrote with a sharpened reed. They mixed soot and water to use as ink.

Today, some museums have examples of hieroglyphics. Language specialists can even read these ancient words.

Check and write.

One of the earliest forms of writing was developed
☐ in old museums.   ☐ in ancient Egypt.
The Egyptians used picture writing called _____ .

syllabic   pictographs

_____ Simple pictures that express an idea

_____ Symbols for sounds or parts of words

Circle.

Egyptians began by   painting / carving   pictures   on their houses. / on stone monuments.

Write T or F.

Egyptians...

___ made "paper" from a papyrus plant.
___ wrote with pencils and pens.
___ made "ink" from soot and water.

• Make up your own hieroglyphic writing.

What About:

A Boomerang

Name_____

Have you ever thrown a boomerang to see if it would spin back to you?

Boomerangs are flat, curved objects that can be thrown for fun or as a sport. But scientists believe that the first boomerangs were made by cavemen and used as weapons.

There are really two kinds of boomerangs—returning and non-returning. A returning boomerang is made to spin through the air in a curve and return to the thrower. It is used mostly for fun or as a sport. The cavemen made non-returning boomerangs. These boomerangs were thrown in a straight path. They were a valuable hunting weapon because they could spin through the air and hit a target harder than a stick or stone could.

Boomerangs were considered so important that they were often decorated and used in ceremonies.

Write and Circle.

A _____ is a flat,   curved   object that can be thrown.
  o r g b o e n a m   straight

Check.

Scientists believe that cavemen
☐ made the first boomerangs.
☐ used boomerangs as weapons.
☐ used boomerangs for cooking.

Write.

The two kinds of boomerangs are _____ and _____.
                                      A   B

Write A or B.

_____ Spins through the air in a straight path

_____ Spins through the air and returns to the thrower

_____ Was a valuable hunting weapon for cavemen

_____ Is used mostly for fun or as a sport

Underline the sentence that tells **why** the boomerang was a valuable weapon.

• Draw a picture showing how boomerangs have been used.

Reading Comprehension IF8708   63   © 1990 Instructional Fair, Inc.

What About:

Quicksand

Many stories of people and animals sinking into quicksand have been told for hundreds of years. Although some of the stories may be true, it helps to understand what quicksand really is.

Quicksand is a deep bed of light, loose sand that is full of water. On the surface it looks much like regular sand, but it is really very different. Regular sand is packed firmly and can be walked on. Because quicksand is loose and full of water, it cannot support much weight.

Quicksand usually develops around rivers and lakes. Water collects in the sand and does not drain away. It continues to collect until the sand becomes soft.

Although some objects can float in quicksand, it cannot support the heavy weight of an animal or person.

Check and write.

Quicksand is a bed of ☐ light ☐ dry ☐ loose sand that is full of _____.

Match.

Regular sand. . .   is loose and full of water.
Quicksand. . .   is packed firmly and can be walked on.

Check.

Quicksand

☐ usually develops in the deserts.
☐ usually develops around rivers and lakes.
☐ cannot support the heavy weight of an animal or person.

True or False

How does quicksand develop?

_____ Water collects in the sand and the sand becomes soft.

_____ Water is drained from the sand and the sand becomes firm.

• Draw a picture showing how quicksand is formed.

What About:

Totem Poles

Totem poles are fascinating to see. They are carved or painted poles featuring people and animals. These carvings are symbols which stand for certain families or tribes. Many totem poles were made by North American Indians to represent the various tribes. Some tribes used birds, fish or animals as their symbols. These symbols are called totems. Many tribes once believed their totems were sacred. Some tribes prayed to their totems. Tribes even took the names of their totems as their tribal names. Often, there were laws against killing the animals which were chosen as totems.

A totem pole was carved to show the symbol, or totem, for a tribe. Totem poles were displayed with pride. Often a tribe would have a feast, called a potlatch, to celebrate a new totem pole.

Underline.

Totem poles show. . .

       symbols which stand for certain families or tribes.

       symbols which stand for famous hunters.

Write.

Many totem poles were made by_____ _____ Indians.

Check.

Some tribes used these as their symbols:

☐ birds ☐ smoke ☐ fish ☐ arrows ☐ animals

Unscramble.

A tribe's symbol is called a _____.

                       e o t t m

True or False

_____ Many tribes believed their totems were sacred.

_____ Some tribes thought their children were totems.

_____ Some tribes prayed to their totems.

_____ Some tribes took their totem's name as their tribal name.

• Design your own totem pole. Write a paragraph about its meaning.

What About:

Galapagos Islands

One of the most fascinating places in the world is the Galapagos Islands, located in the Pacific Ocean just along the equator. The islands lie 650 miles west of Ecuador, a country in South America. The Galapagos Islands, which are made up of fifteen islands, are covered with volcanic peaks.

The islands are famous for several reasons. Long ago, pirates buried their treasures on the islands. The islands were called the Enchanted Islands. But the Galapagos Islands are most famous for the unusual animals and birds which live there. Many of these animals are not found anywhere else in the world. Living on the island are birds that cannot fly, giant turtles that weigh 500 pounds and penguins which are normally only found in the Antarctic. But the most incredible sight on the Galapagos Islands may be the huge lizards, called iguanas. The iguanas often grow to be four feet long!

Check.

The islands are most famous for
- ☐ their unusual sunsets.
- ☐ their unusual animals and birds.

Write, circle and check.

The Galapagos Islands ooo

_____ are covered with _____ peaks.

lie ⟨ 65 / 650 ⟩ miles west of _____ .

are made up of ☐ fifty ☐ fifteen islands.

are located in the _____ Ocean along the ⟨ Arctic. / equator. ⟩

Match.

Living on the islands are . . .

birds	that weigh 500 pounds.
giant turtles	that grow to be four feet long.
penguins	that cannot fly.
lizards	normally only found in the Antarctic.

Underline the sentence that gives a name for the huge lizards.

• Write about what you might find on the Galapagos Islands.

What About:

Stonehenge.

Stonehenge is an ancient monument made of a group of huge stones. It is located in Wiltshire, England. It is not known who put them there or what they really mean. Some scientists believe that they were put there thousands of years ago by people who worshipped the sun.

Through the years, many of the original stones fell or were carried away and used to build other things. But many stones still stand in place. From these stones and other markings, scientists believe they know how the monument looked when it was first built. They believe that it

was a circle of large stones with other stones in the center. These center stones were probably used as an altar. Some scientists believe that Stonehenge was built by ancient people to study the sun. They may have used the monument to predict changes in the seasons—even eclipses of the sun!

Check.

Stonehenge

☐ is an ancient monument made of a group of huge stones.

☐ is located in Wiltshire, England.

☐ was built as a place to study the ocean.

Circle.

Stonehenge may have been built
thousands
hundreds
of years ago.

Underline.

Some scientists believe that Stonehenge . . .

    may have been built as a castle.

    may have been built by sun worshippers.

True or False

_____ Over the years, many of the stones fell or were carried away.

_____ Only five stones remain as a monument.

_____ The center stones were probably used as a house.

_____ Ancient people may have used the monument to study the sun.

• Draw a picture showing how the ancient people used Stonehenge.

What About:

Castles

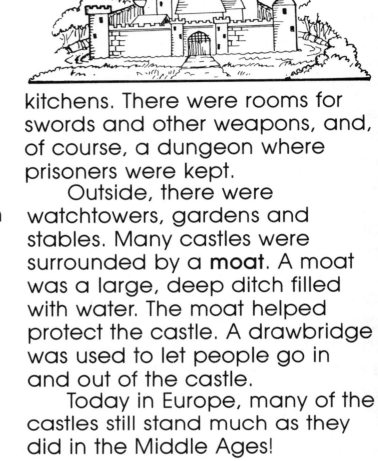

Over a thousand years ago, Europe was living in a time of lords, knights and many wars. This time is called the Middle Ages or the Medieval Period.

During this time, the wealthy lords lived in castles. A castle was a huge building that was often surrounded by a stone wall. But a castle was more than just a home. Because of the many wars, a lord used his castle as a place to protect his family and friends.

Castles had many kinds of rooms. The lord and his family lived in the center of the castle, known as the **keep**. The keep had sleeping rooms, dining rooms, praying rooms and kitchens. There were rooms for swords and other weapons, and, of course, a dungeon where prisoners were kept.

Outside, there were watchtowers, gardens and stables. Many castles were surrounded by a **moat**. A moat was a large, deep ditch filled with water. The moat helped protect the castle. A drawbridge was used to let people go in and out of the castle.

Today in Europe, many of the castles still stand much as they did in the Middle Ages!

Circle.

The keep had rooms for boats / swords and other weapons.

Write and check.

Over a thousand years ago, Europe was living in a time that we call _____ Ages or _____ Period.

This was a time of: ☐ lords ☐ knights ☐ peace ☐ many wars

During the Middle Ages, lords lived in _____.

Check.

Outside, there were: ☐ watchtowers ☐ stables ☐ gardens ☐ kitchens

Circle.

Many castles were surrounded by a large ditch called a moat. / river.

Write.

People were able to cross the moat on a _____.

• Write a story about life in a castle.

What About:
Braille

Have you ever seen a book that is written in braille? Braille is a special system that makes it possible for blind people to read. It is made by a code of dots raised on the paper. A blind person can then read the code by touching the dots.

Braille was developed in 1829 by Louis Braille, a 15-year-old blind student in France. His code is still used today.

Braille code is made from six dots. The dots are placed two across, and three down. From these six dots, many different symbols can be made by raising certain dots. This six-dot code can make the alphabet,

numerals, punctuation marks and more.

Braille material is made by a process that puts the dotted code on metal plates. The plates are then pressed against paper. This forms the dotted code on the paper. Books, magazines and even menus are written in braille.

Check.

Braille
- ☐ is a special system that allows blind people to read.
- ☐ is a code used to send secret messages.

True or False

_____ Braille is made by a code of dots raised on the paper.

_____ Braille is read by touching the dots.

_____ Braille was developed by a blind student.

_____ Braile was developed in Italy in 1829.

Write.

How many dots are used to make the Braille code? _____

Write 1, 2, 3.

How is braille made?

○ The metal plates are pressed against paper.

○ The dotted code is put on metal plates.

○ The dotted code is formed on the paper.

• Write a story of how you think the braille code was developed.

What About:

Hearing Aids

A hearing aid is a wonderful invention that helps improve a person's hearing. There are two basic kinds of hearing aids: air conduction aids and bone conduction aids. The air conduction aid increases the sound and brings it directly into the ear. The bone conduction aid brings the sound waves to the bones behind the ear. The sound vibrations move through the bones into the ear.

People have used "hearing aids" for hundreds of years. One of the first aids was the ear trumpet, which looked like a large funnel. People would hold the ear trumpet to their ear to help them hear.

Name_____

Alexander Graham Bell tried to make a hearing aid. He was unsuccessful, but his work helped him invent something else—the telephone! But his work helped others. In 1902, the first battery-powered hearing aid was invented.

Today, hearing aids use transistors or tiny batteries. This makes hearing aids much smaller and easier to use. Hearing aids can even be made in the earpiece of eyeglasses!

Write.

What are the two basic kinds of hearing aids?

_____ _____ aids   _____ _____ aids

Write and check.

One of the first hearing aids was called an ear_____.

The ear trumpet was shaped like a ☐ bell.
                                    ☐ funnel.

T or F

Alexander Graham Bell invented the first hearing aid.   T   F

In 1902, the first battery-powered hearing aid was invented.   T   F

Hearing aids can be made in the earpiece of eyeglasses.   T   F

Circle.

Modern hearing aids use   trumpet   or   batteries.
                           transistors   funnels.

• Draw a picture showing how the two kinds of hearing aids work.

What About:
Eyeglasses

Name_____

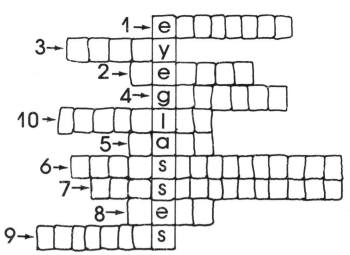

Many people wear eyeglasses to improve their eyesight. Eyeglasses are made with two lenses held together by a frame. Eyeglasses are made in many colors, shapes and sizes.

Eyeglasses may have first been made in Italy in the 1200's. These early glasses were worn by balancing them on the nose! These first glasses probably did little to improve eyesight.

It wasn't until the 1700's that eyeglasses were made which greatly improved eyesight. These glasses were set in frames which had sidepieces that rested on the ears.

Eyeglasses can help people in different ways. Some people cannot see things far away. This is called nearsightedness. Some people cannot see things close to them. This is called farsightedness. Glasses can be worn to correct both problems.

Some people need help seeing things both far and near. Glasses, called bifocals, are made to correct this problem. Bifocals were invented by an American, Benjamin Franklin.

Write.

Many people wear glasses to improve their ¹→ _____ .

Eyeglasses are made with two ²→ _____ held together by a frame.

Eyeglasses may have first been made in ³→ _____ .

Eyeglasses in the 1700's ⁴→ _____ improved eyesight.

These had frames with sidepieces that rested on the ⁵→ _____ .

⁶→ _____ when people cannot see things far away

⁷→ _____ when people cannot see things close to them

Some people need help seeing both far and ⁸→ _____ .

Special glasses, ⁹→ _____ , help people see both far and near.

Bifocals were invented by Benjamin ¹⁰→ _____ .

What About:
Sound

It is easy to take all of the sounds around us for granted. But do you really know what sound is? Sound is caused by something quivering back and forth. This quivering motion is called a vibration. Vibrations travel through the air. You hear them as sounds. The air can carry many vibrations at one time. This is how you can hear many sounds at the same time. Different sounds are created according to how fast something vibrates. The faster it vibrates, the higher the sound. A slower vibration causes a lower sound.

Some unpleasant sounds are called noise. Noise can be harmful to your hearing. Loud noises, such as airplanes or machines, can even cause a hearing loss. But other sounds, such as music or talking, are not dangerous—just pleasant!

Name_____

Unscramble.

_____ is caused by something quivering back and forth.
o d S n u

Check.

Vibrations

☐ travel through the air.
☐ are heard as sounds.
☐ travel through the air one at a time.

Underline.

Different sounds are made by

how hot the air becomes.
how fast something vibrates.

Match.

The faster something vibrates. . .   the lower the sound.
The slower something vibrates. . .   the higher the sound.

Write.

Some unpleasant sounds are _____ . Underline two examples of harmful noise. Circle two examples of pleasant sounds.

• List five pleasant sounds and five noises.

What About:

Ballet

Ballet is one of the most unusual and beautiful dances ever performed. A ballet dancer must be very strong and coordinated to do many of the spins, leaps and turns. But ballet dancers must also be graceful. This allows them to make the difficult moves look easy.

Ballet is for men and women. The women often dance on the tips of their toes.

Ballet began in Italy in the 1400's. The first ballet told stories in dance. The dancers wore fancy costumes. Many of their dances told of Greek myths and legends. This ballet was very

different from today's ballet.

Today's ballet is called classical ballet. It was first developed in France during the 1600's. Special steps and positions made this ballet different from any before. Today's dancers still use the French names for each of these steps and positions.

Unscramble and circle.

_____ is one of the   easiest ways to exercise.
 l B e a l t   most unusual dances ever performed.

Circle and check.

A ballet dancer must be very short / strong and coordinated to do the:

☐ spins ☐ cartwheels ☐ leaps ☐ jumping jacks ☐ spine

True or False

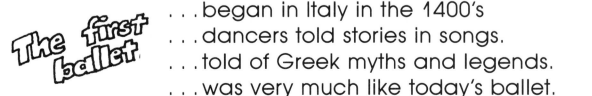

The first ballet

. . .began in Italy in the 1400's	T	F
. . .dancers told stories in songs.	T	F
. . .told of Greek myths and legends.	T	F
. . .was very much like today's ballet.	T	F

Today's ballet

. . .is called classical ballet.	T	F
. . .was first developed in France in the 1600's.	T	F
. . .uses the same steps with Spanish names.	T	F

• Draw a picture of how the first ballet in Italy might have looked.

What About:
Orchestra

Have you ever heard a performance by an orchestra? An orchestra is a group of musicians who play many different kinds of instruments. The most famous kind of orchestra is called a symphony orchestra. It is made up of four main sections: the string section, the woodwind section, the brass section and the percussion section.

The string section is the main part of the orchestra. It is made up of stringed instruments, such as violins, violas, cellos and string basses. The best violinist is called the concertmaster. The concertmaster sometimes acts as the conductor.

The woodwind section is made up of flutes, clarinets, oboes and bassoons.

The brass section is made up of trumpets, French horns, trombones and tubas.

The percussion section is made up of kettledrums, called timpani, bells, cymbals and even a gong!

A symphony is led by a conductor. Through the years, famous composers have written specials works, called symphonies, for orchestras.

Circle.

An   oboe
     orchestra   is a group of musicians who play many instruments.

Write.

The most famous kind of orchestra is called a _____ orchestra.

Unscramble.

Name the four main sections of a symphony orchestra:

_____ section
   d i o n w o w d

_____ section
   s b s a r

_____ section
   g i t s r n

_____ section
   c s n p r u i o s e

Check.

Which section makes up the main part of an orchestra?

☐ woodwind   ☐ string   ☐ percussion

Underline the sentence that tells who leads the orchestra.

• Draw a sketch of an orchestra with its four sections.

What About:

Drama

Drama is a play performed by actors. A drama tells a story. Drama can be serious, or funny, or sometimes both. There are three basic kinds of drama: tragedy, comedy and melodrama.

A tragedy is a drama about a serious subject. Tragedies often deal with the meaning of life, and how people treat each other.

A comedy is a drama that uses feelings of joy. Comedy can also show very exaggerated and ridiculous behavior.

A melodrama is a drama which tells a story of good against evil. A melodrama features an evil villain who tries to destroy the good characters.

Drama is believed to have begun in ancient Greece. The

Greeks performed their plays in outdoor theaters. Many of the Greek tragedies were about myths. Drama was later popular in many countries; Italy, England, Spain, France, India, China and Japan. Today, drama is popular in practically every country in the world.

Circle and check.

Drama . . . is a
  costume
  play
performed by actors.

. . . tells a: ☐ joke ☐ part ☐ story

. . . can be serious, or funny, or both. T F

Write.

Drama is believed to have begun in ancient _____.

The Greeks performed their dramas in _____ theaters.

Many of the Greek tragedies were about _____.

Underline the sentence that tells which countries performed dramas.

• Write a plot or story for each of the three kinds of drama.

What About:

Opera

What do you think of when you hear the word opera? Do you think of singing, fancy costumes and orchestra music? Opera is all of these things, and more! Opera is a play in which the actors sing most of their lines. Often, dancers appear in operas.

Music is very important in an opera. It expresses the emotions of the story—feelings of sadness, joy and love.

An opera is made up of two parts: the libretto and the music. The libretto is the story or words of an opera. Many people read the libretto of an opera before they see the performance. This helps them follow the story as it is sung. The music of an opera includes the singers, the

orchestra and the conductor. An opera singer must not only be an excellent singer, but also an actor, and sometimes a dancer as well. The orchestra provides the background music for the entire opera. And the conductor has the job of keeping the singers and the orchestra together.

Opera began in Florence, Italy, in the late 1500's, and is still very popular today.

Unscramble and circle.

_____ is a play in which
r a O p e

actors speak most of their lines.
actors sing most of their lines.

Circle.

The music in an opera expresses the

costumes
emotions
of the story.

Write.

An opera has two parts: _____ and _____
                                           A   B

Write A or B.

_____ Includes the singers, orchestra and conductor

_____ The story or words of an opera

True or False

_____ Opera began in the late 1700's in Paris, France.

_____ Opera began in the late 1500's in Florence, Italy.

• Draw a picture showing how an opera might look.

What About:

Vaccinations

Not many years ago, people became very ill from many diseases such as polio, whooping cough, measles and smallpox. Today, these diseases are very rare because of vaccinations. A vaccination is a way of protecting a person from a disease. Most vaccinations are given by an injection.

Diseases are caused by certain germs, either viruses or bacteria. When these germs enter the body, the body fights back by making antibodies. After a person is well, some of the antibodies remain in the body to protect it from becoming ill with the disease again.

Vaccinations work in much the same way. A vaccination helps the body prepare for a disease by putting a few weak disease germs into the body. This causes the body to make antibodies to fight the germs. So when the actual strong disease germs attack the body, the body is ready to fight back. Because of the vaccination, the body has antibodies ready to protect it from the disease.

Write.

A _____ is a way of protecting a person from a disease.

Circle.

Most vaccinations are given by an   x-ray.
                                     injection.

Check.

Before there were vaccinations, people became very ill from diseases such as: ☐ polio   ☐ whooping cough   ☐ measles   ☐ broken arm   ☐ small pox   ☐ earache

Write.

The body fights disease germs by making _____ .

T or F

A Vaccination...

puts a few, weak disease germs into the body.   T   F

causes the body to make antibodies to protect itself.   T   F

is used to protect the body from antibodies.   T   F

helps the body prepare to fight the strong disease germs.   T   F

• Write about how your life is different because of vaccinations.

What About:

A Microscope

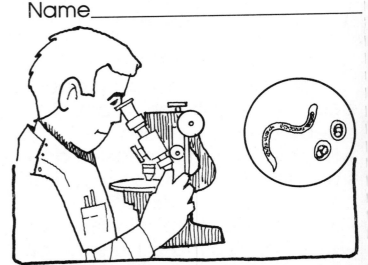

Have you ever looked into a microscope? A microscope is an instrument that helps us see very small things. A microscope magnifies these things. This means that they appear much larger than they really are. Scientists and doctors can use microscopes to study parts of the body, such as blood and skin cells. They also can study germs, and tiny plants and animals.

A microscope works much like a magnifying glass. But, while a magnifying glass has only one lens, a microscope has two sets of lenses. They are called the objective lens and the ocular lens.

Through the years, people used glass lenses to help them see many small things. But in 1590, a Dutchman discovered how to use two lenses to magnify things and invented the first true microscope.

Check.

A microscope

☐ is an instrument that helps us see tiny things.

☐ is an instrument that helps us see the stars.

☐ magnifies tiny things so that they appear much larger

Scientists can study: ☐ blood and skin cells ☐ large rooms

☐ germs ☐ comets ☐ tiny plants and animals

Write.

A microscope works much like a _____ glass.

Match, write and circle.

magnifying glass   two sets of lenses

microscope   only one lens

What are the names of the two microscope lenses?

_____ lens   _____ lens

The first microscope was invented by a   Dutchman   in   1590.
                                                       Frenchman   1950.

• List three ways that doctors can use microscopes to help you.

What About:

Dry Ice

Do you know how dry ice got its name or for what it is used? Dry ice is the name for solid carbon dioxide. Carbon dioxide is a chemical.

You know that when regular ice melts, it changes from a solid piece of ice into a liquid. But dry ice does not melt into a liquid. It changes from a solid piece of ice into a gas. Dry ice can be as cold as − 112°. That is much colder than ordinary ice. Although it is safe to eat ordinary ice, dry ice can cause death if eaten. That is because it is so extremely cold.

What is dry ice used for? It is used to refrigerate many things that need to be kept cold. Many foods are packed and sent from place to place in dry ice. Because dry ice does not melt, it can keep food frozen for several days.

Underline and write.

Dry Ice   is the name for solid water.
             is the name for solid carbon dioxide.

Carbon dioxide is a _____.

Match.

Regular ice. . .   changes from a solid piece of ice into a gas.
Dry ice. . .   changes from a solid piece of ice into a liquid.

Check.

Dry ice...
☐ can be as cold as −112°.
☐ is much colder than ordinary ice.
☐ is safe to eat.
☐ can cause death if eaten.

Circle.

Dry ice is used to melt refrigerate many foods that need to be kept cold.

Write.

Because dry ice does not _____, it can keep foods frozen.

• Write about uses for regular ice and dry ice.

79

What About:
Bacteria

Name_____

Bacteria are among the smallest forms of life. They are made of only **one** cell. They are so tiny that they can only be seen with a microscope. A single bacteria is called a bacterium.

Bacteria can be found almost everywhere—in the air, in the ocean and in the soil. They can even be found inside our bodies.

Some bacteria can be helpful. For example, bacteria can help people digest certain foods. Bacteria can also help keep the ground rich in nitrogen so plants can grow. Bacteria is even used to help make cheese, buttermilk and vinegar.

Other bacteria can be harmful.

Certain bacteria can cause diseases, such as pneumonia or whooping cough. Bacteria can also cause food to spoil.

Scientists put bacteria into four groups. They are grouped according to their shape. The four bacteria shapes are: round, rod-shaped, bent-rod shaped and spiral-shaped.

Underline.

Bacteria   are among the longest forms of life.
are among the smallest forms of life.

Circle T or F.

Some bacteria may be helpful, some may be harmful.   T   F

Write helpful or harmful.

_____ Bacteria can help people digest certain foods.

_____ Bacteria can cause diseases, such as pneumonia.

_____ Bacteria keeps the ground rich in nitrogen for plants to grow.

_____ Bacteria can cause food to spoil.

_____ Bacteria is used to help make cheese, buttermilk and vinegar.

Check.

The four shapes of bacteria are:

☐ round ☐ square ☐ rod ☐ bent-rod ☐ oval ☐ spiral ☐ triangle

• Make a list of places where bacteria could be found.

What About:

Sponges

Name_____

Sponges are fascinating to see and touch. People once thought that sponges were plants, but now we know that they are really animals.

Sponges live in oceans. They are attached to the bottom of the ocean so they do not move around.

A sponge is very different from any other animal. It has no mouth, heart or stomach. Its body is covered with tiny pores which allow food and water to pass through. Sponges have skeletons, but they are not made of bones. Some are made of tiny needles. Others are made of fibers.

Living sponges in the ocean can be found in all shapes and sizes. Many are bright shades of red, blue and yellow.

In some places, sponge fishermen dive deep into the ocean and pull the sponges from the ocean floor. They are dried in the sun before being sold. These sponges are excellent for cleaning.

T or F

Sponges

. . .were once thought to be plants.   T   F

. . .are really animals.   T   F

. . .live on the top of lakes and streams.   T   F

. . .are attached to the bottom of oceans. T   F

Circle and check.

Sponges have   skeletons / ears   made of ☐ needles. ☐ bones. ☐ fibers.

Unscramble.

Living sponges in the ocean grow in all _____ and _____
                                                             e p s a h s   z s s i e

Underline the sentence that tells the colors of many sponges.

Write.

Sponge fishermen sell sponges to be used for _____.

• Write about sponges living on the ocean floor.

Reading Comprehension IF8708   81   © 1990 Instructional Fair, Inc.

What About:
Dyes

Can you imagine how dull everything around you would seem without color? Dye is a substance that gives color to many things. For over 5000 years, people have used dyes. Until the mid-1800's, only natural dyes were used. These dyes came from different parts of plants, such as the bark, roots, berries or flowers. Certain plants produced certain colors. The indigo plant produced a blue dye. The madder plant produced bright red and brown dyes. The bark and leaves of oak, maple and walnut trees were used to make yellow, orange and black dyes.

In 1856, an eighteen-year-old boy in England discovered how to make dyes from chemicals. Chemical dyes were called synthetic. This means that they are man-made, not natural. Today, almost all dyes are synthetic.

But how does dye work? Dye dissolves into a liquid when it is wet. This colored liquid is absorbed, or taken in, by the threads of the material. Some dyes will never fade. They are called fast dyes. Today's synthetic dyes are made in thousands of beautiful shades.

Write.

_____ is a substance that gives color to many things.

Circle.

People have used dyes for over
500
5000
years.

Check.

Natural dyes came from parts of plants, such as:

☐ bark ☐ chemicals ☐ berries ☐ roots ☐ flowers

Match.

Where did each color come from?

indigo plant   yellow, orange and black

madder plant   blue

oak, maple and walnut trees   red and brown

• List fifteen things which can be colored with dye.

What About:

A Mirror

Have you ever wondered how you can "see yourself" in a mirror? Most mirrors are glass, but they can be any smooth surface that can reflect, or give back, light. When light strikes a mirror in a certain pattern, the light is reflected back in the same pattern. So when you stand in front of a mirror, your image is reflected back for you to see.

Long ago, people used polished brass, silver and gold to see their reflections. But for almost four hundreds years, people have made mirrors from plate glass. The front of the glass is polished. The back is painted with a substance that reflects light. The glass is then cut into many sizes to be used as mirrors. A flat mirror reflects a correct image. If the mirror is wavy or curved, the image will look odd. This is why people look so funny in the wavy mirrors used in carnivals!

Unscramble and underline.

A _____ is   any surface that has a pattern on it.
   r m r o i r   any smooth surface that reflects light.

Check.

When light strikes a mirror in a certain pattern. . .

☐ the light is reflected back in the same pattern.
☐ the light stays in the mirror.

Circle and check.

For almost four / nine hundred years, people have made mirrors from:

☐ plastic   ☐ plate glass   ☐ brass

Write 1, 2, 3.

How are mirrors made?

◯ The back is painted with a substance that reflects light.
◯ The glass is cut into many sizes.
◯ The front of the glass is polished.

• Write about how you would look in a curved mirror.

What About:

Diamonds

Everyone knows how beautiful diamonds can be. But did you know that a diamond is the hardest substance found in nature? Diamonds are crystals made of carbon. Scientists believe that diamonds were formed long ago when parts of the Earth were under great pressure and heat. Diamonds are so hard that they are used to cut many other hard materials. But a diamond can only be cut by another diamond, or by a man-made material called borazon.

Diamonds are found in just a few places in the world. Miners must dig into the earth to remove the diamonds. Sometimes tons of earth must be removed and crushed to find just one small diamond.

Some of the diamonds are used in industry to cut hard materials. Other diamonds are polished and cut to become jewels.

There have been many famous diamonds in history. The largest, found in 1905, weighed one and one-third pounds!

Write.

A _____ is the hardest substance found in nature.

Circle and check.

Diamonds are   crystals / glass   made of ☐ plastic. / ☐ carbon.

Write.

A diamond can only be cut. . .

by another_____.

or by a man-made material called _____.

Check.

Diamonds
☐ are found in just a few places in the world.
☐ are found lying close to the top of the ground.
☐ can be used in industry or as jewels.
☐ are only used to make jewelry.

Underline the sentence that describes the largest diamond found.

• Draw a picture to show how diamonds are removed from the earth.

What About:

Plastics

Did you know that hundreds of things around you each day are made of plastic? Plastics are made from chemicals. They can be made in any color or shape. Plastics may be hard or soft. Hard plastics are used to make furniture, televisions, football helmets and floors. Soft plastics are used to make toys, laundry baskets, garden hoses and food bags.

Plastics have special uses in many jobs. They are used in factories to hold machines together. Builders use plastics that are made to look like wood or marble. Doctors mend bones with plastic parts and sew up wounds with plastic thread.

Plastics are made in special plants by using chemicals from coal, petroleum and natural gas. These chemicals are heated to change them into a material called resin. Resin is later melted and shaped into all the many plastic products around you.

True or False

Plastic facts:

_____ Plastics are made from chemicals.

_____ Plastics are made in just one color and shape.

_____ Hundreds of things around you are made of plastic.

_____ Plastics may be hard or soft.

Mark . . . ✓ products made from hard plastics.

☒ products made from soft plastics.

☐ furniture ☐ food bags ☐ garden hoses ☐ football helmets
☐ laundry baskets ☐ floors ☐ toys ☐ television

Write.

Plastics are made by heating chemicals from:

_____, _____ and _____ _____.

The heated chemicals change into a material called _____.

• List all the plastic products that you see around you.

85

What About:
Mold

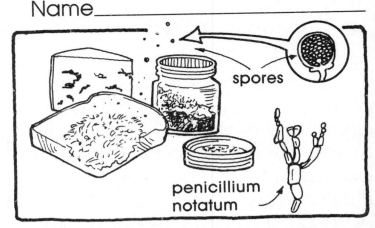

spores

penicillium notatum

Perhaps you have seen a green fuzzy spot on bread or cheese. If so, it was probably mold. Mold is a kind of plant called fungi. The most common molds are green or black. Mold likes to grow in a moist, warm place. But where does it come from?

Mold comes from spores which exist in the air. If they find a moist, warm place, they will produce mold. Mold grows in webs of fuzzy branches. It continues to grow as long as the conditions are right.

Foods, such as cheese, fruit, bread and preserves, can develop mold if they are left out in a warm, damp room. Mold may even grow on leather shoes, belts or furniture.

Mold is usually thought of as a problem. But some molds are valuable to scientists. The most famous mold is called penicillium notatum. This mold is used to make a valuable drug called penicillin.

Unscramble and check.

_____ is a kind of plant called
d M l o

☐ fern.
☐ fungi.

Circle.

The most common molds are: red   green   blue   black

Write.

Molds like to grow in a _____, _____ place.

Check.

Mold

☐ comes from spores, which exist in the air.
☐ likes to grow in cool, dry places.
☐ grows in webs of fuzzy branches.

True or False

_____ Mold can even grow on leather shoes, belts or furniture.

_____ Mold is **always** thought of as a problem.

Underline the name of the most famous mold.
Put a circle around the name of the drug made from this mold.

• Draw a picture showing where and how mold can grow.

What About:
Thermometer

A thermometer is an instrument that is used to measure the temperature of something. Thermometers can be used to measure the temperature of a room, a liquid, the air—or even a person!

The most common type of thermometer uses a liquid in a glass column. Mercury is the liquid most often used. The mercury will rise in the column as the temperature rises. It will fall in the column as the temperature falls. When the mercury reaches the same temperature level as the substance it is measuring, it stays still.

The temperature scales on most thermometers are either

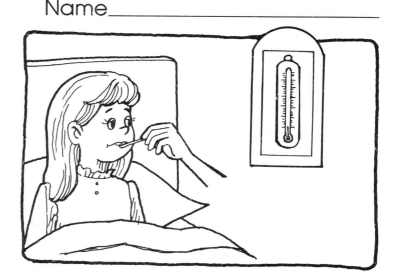

Fahrenheit or Celsius. Fahrenheit has a freezing point at 32 degrees (32°). Celsius has a freezing point at 0 degrees (0°).

The first thermometer was called a thermoscope. It was made in 1593. The first mercury thermometer was made in 1714 by a man named Gabriel Fahrenheit. The Fahrenheit scale is named for him.

Underline.

A thermometer. . .

    is an instrument used to measure the moisture in the air.

    is an instrument used to measure the temperature of something.

Match.

Mercury will rise in the column. . .   as the temperature falls.

Mercury will fall in the column. . .   as the temperature rises.

The two scales most often used on thermometers are:

_____ and _____
         A   B

Write A or B.

_____ This scale has a freezing point of 0 degrees (0°).

_____ This scale has a freezing point of 32 degrees (32°).

Underline the name of the **first** thermometer. Circle the name of the man who made the first **mercury** thermometer.

• Draw a Fahrenheit and Celsius thermometer. Show the correct freezing point on each.

What About:

Matches

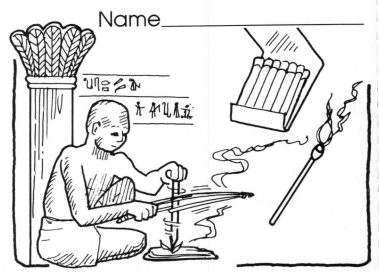

It is hard to imagine how important fire was to people living thousands of years ago. It was necessary in order for people to keep warm, and to cook. Through the years, people developed ways of starting fires. Cave people used flint, a hard rock, to start a fire. The Egyptians rubbed a bow drill on wood to make a spark of fire. The Greeks rubbed pieces of buckthorn and bay together to produce a fire.

Today, it is easy to create a fire by using matches. Matches are made with special chemicals that allow them to start a fire. The first chemical to be used was phosphorus, which burns at a low temperature. There are two basic kinds of matches—friction matches and safety matches.

Friction matches are made by covering the tip of a match with layers of chemicals and wax. When the match is struck, the chemicals "explode" and the wax and wood or paper match begins to burn.

Safety matches are made with chemicals, too. But they will not burn unless they are struck on a special material.

Write A, B or C.

How did people long ago start fires?

A—cave people   B—Egyptians   C—Greeks

_____ Rubbed pieces of buckthorn and bay together

_____ Used a hard rock called flint

_____ Rubbed a bow drill on wood

Circle.

The two basic kinds of matches are: friction   chemical   safety

True or False

_____ Friction matches are made with chemicals and wax.

_____ Safety matches are made with flint and wax.

_____ Friction matches will only burn when wet.

_____ Safety matches must be struck on a special material.

• Draw a picture showing why cave people needed fire.

What About:
Aluminum

When you use aluminum foil, do you think of it as a metal? Aluminum is a light, but strong, silver metal. It is an amazing metal which can be rolled or formed into any shape. It is waterproof, rustproof and light-weight. It is no wonder that it is called **magic metal!**

Aluminum is not found as a natural metal in the soil. It is made from bauxite ore. After the bauxite ore is taken from the ground, it is sent to a special plant. There it is washed and crushed into a powder. The powder is mixed with a solution to remove the impurities. Then it is processed into alumina, a dry white powder. The alumina is made into aluminum.

Aluminum may have first been used thousands of years ago in Iraq. The people used clay soil which contained aluminum ore. They beat the soil into flat sheets. They formed the pieces into bowls and utensils. But it wasn't until the 1800's that aluminum was discovered as a metal. A Danish chemist made the first aluminum in 1825.

Today, plants produce millions of metric tons of aluminum every year. Aluminum is used to make everything from toys to buildings!

Check.

Which words describe the metal aluminum?

☐ silver   ☐ rustproof   ☐ gold   ☐ strong
☐ heavy   ☐ light   ☐ waterproof   ☐ rusty

Write 1, 2, 3, 4, 5.

How is aluminum made?

◯ The powder is mixed with a solution to remove the impurities.
◯ Bauxite ore is taken from the ground and sent to a special plant.
◯ The alumina is made into aluminum.
◯ A process changes the mixture into alumina.
◯ The bauxite ore is washed and crushed into a powder.

• Make a list of things that aluminum could be used for.

What About:

Glue

You can use glue for so many things—for repairs, for building, or for art activities. But do you know what glue is and how it is made?

Glue is a material, called adhesive, which is used to stick things together. There are three basic kinds of glue: hide glue, bone glue and fish glue. The glues are made of gelatin, which comes from boiling animal parts and bones.

Long ago, people used other materials as glue. Ancient people used sticky juices from plants and insects. This was mixed with vegetable coloring

and used as paint on rocks and caves. Egyptians learned to boil animal hides and bones to make glue. This was much like the glue that is used today.

Today, there are many special kinds of glue. Epoxy glue is made to stick in high temperatures, even if it becomes wet. "Super" glue is the strongest of glues. It can stick even with two tons of pressure against it.

Unscramble and underline.

_____ is a material used   to make animal hides and bones.
l e u G   to stick things together.

Write.

The three basic kinds of glue are:

_____ glue   _____ glue   _____ glue

Check.

Glue is a special material called ☐ adhesive.
                                   ☐ rubber.

T or F

Long ago . . . people used sticky juices from plants.   T   F
. . . Egyptians boiled animal hides and bones.   T   F
. . . Egyptians made glue much different from glue today.   T   F

Match.

Epoxy glue . . .   can stick even against two tons of pressure.
"Super" glue . . .   is made to stick at high temperatures or if wet.

• List 10 ways that you could use glue.

What About:

Barbed Wire

Everyone knows what barbed wire is, but do you know why it was such an important invention?

Before barbed wire was invented in 1873, many farmers and ranchers planted shrubs as a fence to keep their cattle from wandering away. They mostly planted osage orange, a thick shrub covered with thorns. This method was often unsuccessful. Other farmers used a plain wire fence, but their cattle could break through and escape.

In 1873, a farmer named Joseph Glidden, invented a new kind of wire fence, called barbed wire. He fastened pieces of short wire barbs onto the plain wire of a fence. This made it painful for cattle if they tried to push through the fence. Glidden's invention was a huge success. It meant that farmers could now let their cattle graze in an area away from the crops. And now, cattle would not wander away and get on the railroad tracks. This helped railroad companies build railroads in the new western territory. So, in many ways, the simple invention of barbed wire helped settle the western frontier.

Circle, write and check.

Before barbed wire,

. . . many farmers and ranchers planted shrubs / wheat as a fence.

. . . many farmers and ranchers planted _____ orange, a shrub. which was covered with ☐ thorns. ☐ large leaves.

. . . many farmers and ranchers used a plain _____ fence.

. . . most shrubs and fences were not / were successful in holding cattle.

T or F

Barbed wire kept cattle away from the crops.	T	F
Barbed wire kept cattle off the railroad tracks.	T	F
Barbed wire helped settle the western frontier.	T	F
Barbed wire was used to build railroads.	T	F

● Write about a ranch before and after barbed wire was invented.

What About:
Dynamite

Perhaps you have seen a cartoon which shows a stick of dynamite with its fuse burning slowly down until . . . boom! This may seem funny in a cartoon, but dynamite is no laughing matter. Dynamite is the most powerful explosive in the world!

Dynamite is mostly used to blast away earth. This is needed to build dams, make foundations for large buildings and for mining.

Dynamite is made of a chemical named nitroglycerin. The word dynamite comes from a Greek word meaning power.

Dynamite was first produced in 1867 by Alfred Nobel. Nobel was a Swedish chemist. His first dynamite was dangerous to use because it exploded so easily.

He later developed a way of mixing nitroglycerin with a chalky-like soil. He placed this mixture into hollow tubes, or sticks. This stick dynamite was safer because it would not explode until a blasting cap was added. Nobel later invented a special dynamite, called blasting gelatin, that would explode under water.

Today, there are over 200 kinds of dynamite!

Circle and write.

Dynamite . . . is made of a chemical named   gelatin.
nitroglycerin.

. . . gets its name from a Greek word meaning _____ .

. . . was first produced in   1867
1687   by a chemist, _____ _____ .

Write 1, 2.

Nobel made his new dynamite safer by:

◯ placing the mixture into hollow tubes, or sticks.

◯ mixing nitroglycerin with a chalky-like soil.

Underline the sentence that tells why the stick dynamite was safer. Circle the sentence that tells the name of the dynamite made for underwater.

• Find out what else Alfred Nobel is famous for.

What About:

An Elevator

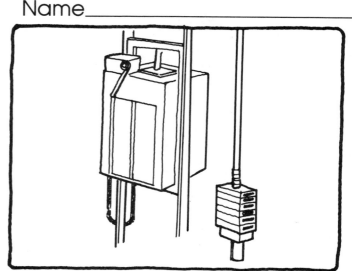

Can you imagine what many city buildings would be like without elevators? An elevator takes people from floor to floor in a building.

Even in ancient times, people found ways of lifting things or people. In Egypt, building material for the pyramids was probably raised on a kind of hand-held elevator. But, it wasn't until the mid-1850's, that a safe elevator was invented by Elisha Otis. His elevator was powered by steam. It featured safety springs which kept the platform from falling. By the end of the 1800's, electric elevators were being used.

Today, elevators are run by electricity. The elevator moves up and down in a shaft. An electric motor at the top of the shaft raises and lowers the elevator.

Modern elevators can carry people up over 1000 stories high. Some buildings put their elevators on the outside of the building to give riders a special view!

Underline.

An elevator   takes people from room to room in a building.
takes people from floor to floor in a building.

Check.

Long ago

☐ Egyptians rode in steel elevators.
☐ people found ways of lifting things.
☐ Egyptians raised materials on hand-held elevators.

True or False

_____ The first safe elevator was invented in the 1700's.

_____ Elisha Otis made the first safe elevator in the mid-1850's.

_____ Elisha Otis's elevator was powered by steam.

_____ The elevator had wheels to keep the platform from falling.

_____ The elevator had safety springs to keep the platform from falling.

• Write about how a city might look if there were no elevators.

What About:

Marco Polo

It is difficult to imagine what the world was like in 1254. Most of Europe was living in an age that we call the Medieval Period. It was a time of castles, knights and nobles, swords and lances and many wars.

It was in that time that Marco Polo was born in Venice, Italy. Life in Venice was different from life in most of Europe. Venice was a city of beautiful buildings and water canals. Many merchants brought riches from other countries to trade in Venice. Marco Polo's father and uncle were merchants. They had traveled to a far-off country called Cathay. Cathay is now called China. There they had become friends with the great ruler, Kublai Khan. He invited them to return again.

When Marco Polo was seventeen years old, he began a journey to China with his father and uncle. They sailed the Indian Ocean and crossed the deserts and mountains of Asia on camels. The journey to China took three years!

Kublai Khan greeted the Polos and showered them with gifts. He was especially impressed with Marco, who could speak four languages.

The Khan sent Marco on many trips through China. On these trips, he saw many amazing things that he had never seen in Europe, such as: coal used as fuel, paper money instead of coins, compasses, papermaking and printing. Marco made many notes about life in China.

After almost twenty years in China, the Polos began their journey home to Italy. Kublai Khan gave them many gifts of ivory, silk, jewels and jade.

When they returned to Venice, they found their city at war. Marco Polo was put in prison. He spent his time writing a book about his years in China. The book is called **Descriptions of the World**. It became the most popular book in Europe. Because of the book, many people in Europe learned about life in China.

• Write about some of the "wonders" that Marco Polo saw in China.

94

Marco Polo

Name_____

Check.

The Medieval Period was a time of:

☐ castles ☐ knights ☐ swords ☐ lances
☐ skyscrapers ☐ nobles ☐ railroads ☐ wars

Circle.

Marco Polo was born in   Rome,   Italy.
                          Venice,

Unscramble.

China was ruled by the great _____ _____.
                              u a K b i l   n h a K

True or False

____ When Marco Polo was seventeen, he traveled to China.

____ Marco Polo traveled to China with his brother.

____ The journey to China took four years.

____ Kublai Khan was glad to see Marco and his father and brother.

____ Marco Polo could speak four languages.

____ Marco Polo only saw one city in China.

Check.

What are some of the amazing things that Marco Polo saw in China?

☐ coal used as fuel   ☐ lightbulbs
☐ windmills   ☐ papermaking
☐ paper money   ☐ hot-air balloons
☐ compasses   ☐ printing

Circle.

Marco Polo returned home after almost   35   years in China.
                                        20

Write.

Kublai Khan gave the Polos gifts of _____, _____, _____

and _____.

Check.

On his return to Venice,   ☐ Marco Polo was made king.
                           ☐ Marco Polo was put in jail.

Write.

While in jail, Marco Polo wrote about his years in _____.

The name of Marco Polo's book was _____.

What About:

Vasco de Balboa

On September 25, 1513, Vasco de Balboa saw something that no other European had ever seen before—the Pacific Ocean.

Balboa saw the ocean from a mountaintop in Central America. He reached the ocean a few days later and claimed it for his country of Spain. Balboa called the ocean the South Sea. A few years later another explorer, Ferdinand Magellan, named the South Sea the Pacific Ocean.

Balboa was born in Spain in 1480. As he grew up, he heard stories about Columbus discovering America. In 1501, Balboa left Spain and sailed to Hispaniola, an island near South America. He did not find the riches he was looking for. He later left the island and traveled to a part of Central America called Darien. Balboa was made governor of Darien.

While in Darien, Balboa heard stories of great treasures to the south. In 1513, he left Darien to search for these treasures. It was during this trip that Balboa discovered the Pacific Ocean. This discovery brought Balboa riches he had not expected to find. As he explored the coast of the Pacific Ocean, he discovered valuable pearls and gold.

Balboa was excited with his new discovery. But when he returned to Darien, he found that a new governor, named Pedrarias, had replaced him.

Balboa moved to a new site and built a city. He built new ships for exploration. But Pedrarias became very jealous of Balboa's popularity. In 1518, he accused Balboa of treason. Balboa was innocent, but he was arrested and jailed.

Pedrarias, as governor, was very powerful. He sentenced Balboa to death. In January of 1519, Balboa was beheaded.

But, almost 500 years later, we still remember Balboa for his great discovery—the Pacific Ocean.

• Write about how Balboa first discovered the Pacific Ocean.

Vasco de Balboa

Name_____

1 → On September 25, 1513, Vasco de Balboa discovered the _____ Ocean.

2 → Balboa saw the ocean from a mountaintop in _____ America.

3 → Balboa called the ocean _____ Sea.

4 → Balboa claimed the Pacific Ocean for _____ .

Write 1, 2, 3, 4, 5.

◯ In 1501, Balboa left Spain and sailed to Hispaniola.

◯ Balboa was made governor of Darien.

◯ Balboa was born in Spain in 1480.

◯ Balboa later traveled to a part of Central America called Darien.

◯ As he grew up, Balboa heard stories about Columbus discovering America.

Underline.

While in Darien,

Balboa heard stories of great treasures in Italy.

Balboa heard stories of great treasures to the south.

Check.

While looking for these treasures, Balboa . . .

☐ discovered a lost city.   ☐ discovered the Pacific Ocean.

Write.

The new governor was named _____ .

Circle T or F.

Balboa

. . . moved to a new site and built a city and ships.	T	F
. . . sailed back to Spain and became governor.	T	F
. . . was accused of treason and placed in jail.	T	F
. . . was guilty of treason.	T	F
. . . was sentenced to death by Pedrarias.	T	F
. . . was beheaded in January of 1519.	T	F
. . . is remembered for discovering the Pacific Ocean.	T	F

What About:
Ferdinand Magellan

The early 1500's were an exciting time of exploration and discovery. Many explorers were looking for new routes to distant lands. During this time, a young nobleman, named Ferdinand Magellan, became excited over the idea of exploring new lands. Magellan had studied geography. He believed that he could find the Spice Islands by sailing just a little west of America.

Magellan traveled to Spain to tell King Charles I of his plan. The king agreed to give Magellan ships and supplies. In return, he asked Magellan to claim the Spice Islands for Spain.

On September 21, 1519, Magellan and 240 men sailed from Spain in five boats: Concepcion, San Antonio, Santiago, Trinidad and Victoria. Magellan sailed across the Atlantic Ocean to South America. He sailed along the coast of South America looking for a place to sail through to the other side of the land. He found a passage near the tip of South America. This passage led from the Atlantic Ocean to another ocean.

Today this passage is called the Strait of Magellan. Magellan named this other ocean the Pacific Ocean, because the waters were so calm.

By the time Magellan reached the Pacific Ocean, he had only three ships left. The San Antonio had secretly sailed back to Spain. The Santiago had wrecked in a storm.

Magellan expected to find the Spice Islands soon after entering the Pacific Ocean. But the three ships sailed west day after day. Many sailors died of hunger or disease. Finally, they reached the Philippine Islands. It was here that Magellan was killed in 1521.

Magellan's ships and crew finally reached the Spice Islands. But as they sailed home to Spain, the Trinidad and the Concepcion were wrecked by storms. On September 6, 1522, three years after leaving Spain, the Victoria arrived back home. It had sailed around the world!

Although Magellan did not live to complete the voyage, he is known as the first man to sail around the world. It was his voyage that first **proved** that the Earth is round.

• Draw a picture of each of Magellan's five ships. Write a sentence under each ship telling what happened to it on the voyage.

Ferdinand Magellan

Name_____

Circle.

Ferdinand Magellan studied
music
geography
as a young man.

Magellan believed that he could find the Spice Islands
    by sailing west of America.   by sailing to India.

Circle, write and check.

Magellan traveled to
sea
Spain
to tell King _____ of his plan.

King Charles agreed to give Magellan:
☐ ships ☐ spice
☐ Italy ☐ supplies

Underline.

King Charles asked Magellan . . .
    to claim the Spice Islands for Spain.
    to take spices to America.

Write.

Magellan and his crew sailed from
Spain in five boats named:

_____   _____

_____   _____

_____

Unscramble, circle, check and write.

Magellan

. . .sailed across the Atlantic Ocean to _____ America.
        o h S u t

. . .looked for a place to sail through to the other side.   T   F

. . .found a
trail
passage
near the tip of South America.

. . .sailed through this passage to a new
☐ island.
☐ ocean.

. . .named the new ocean the _____ Ocean.

The passage that Magellan discovered is now called
the _____ of _____ .

Match.

San Antonio   shipwrecked in a storm.
Santiago   secretly sailed back to Spain.

Magellan is known as the _____ man to sail around the _____ .

What About:

Hernando Cortez

From an age of great explorers, Hernando Cortez is one of the most famous. Cortez was born in Spain in 1485. His father wanted him to study law, but Cortez wanted to seek riches and adventure.

In 1504, Cortez left Spain and sailed across the Atlantic Ocean to the island of Cuba. There he heard rumors of a rich Indian empire in Mexico. The Spanish governor of Cuba sent Cortez to find this rich empire. Cortez left Cuba with eleven ships and 600 men to help him.

When Cortez landed in Mexico, he learned that the country was ruled by Aztec Indians. The Aztecs had many enemies in Mexico. With their help, Cortez set out to conquer the Aztecs. They marched through the jungle to the Aztec capital. There they found the Aztec ruler, Montezuma. Cortez imprisoned Montezuma and captured the city. For a while, many Aztecs believed that Cortez was the Aztec god who had come to Earth.

Cortez and his men discovered beauty and riches in the Aztec city. It was filled with stone towers, gardens and canals.

Later, while Cortez was away from the city, fighting broke out between his men and the Aztecs. Cortez and his followers were finally forced out of the city.

The next year, Cortez returned with an army of thousands and attacked the Aztecs. Cortez and his men cut off the food and water supply to the city. They destroyed many of the buildings. After a few weeks of fighting, the Aztecs surrendered. Much of the treasures and riches from the city was shipped back to Spain. It had taken Cortez twelve years to conquer and control the Aztec Empire.

Cortez later explored much of Central America. In 1528, he returned to Spain where King Charles I gave him the title of marquis.

• Draw a picture showing how the Aztec city may have looked.

True or False.

Hernando Cortez...

_____ is one of the most famous explorers from long ago.

_____ was born in Spain in 1485.

_____ wanted to study law, just as his father wanted.

_____ wanted to seek riches and adventure.

_____ left Spain in 1504 and sailed across the Pacific Ocean.

_____ landed in Cuba where he heard rumors of a rich empire in Mexico.

Circle and check.

The Spanish king / governor of Cuba ☐ sent Cortez to find the empire. ☐ gave Cortez all of Mexico.

Circle and write.

Cortez left France / Cuba with ____ ships and ____ men.

Write 1, 2, 3, 4, 5.

What happened when Cortez reached Mexico?

◯ Cortez and his followers marched through the jungle to the Aztec capital.

◯ Cortez imprisoned Montezuma and captured the city.

◯ Cortez landed in Mexico where he learned that the land was ruled by Aztecs.

◯ Cortez found Montezuma, the Aztec ruler.

◯ Cortez asked the Aztecs' enemies to help him.

Check.

What did Cortez find in the Aztec city?

☐ beauty   ☐ steam engines   ☐ stone towers   ☐ riches
☐ gardens   ☐ canals   ☐ printing machines

Write and check.

Cortez and his men . . .

cut off the _____ and _____ supply to the city.

destroyed ☐ ships. ☐ buildings.

caused the Aztecs to ☐ win. ☐ surrender.

shipped the Aztec riches back to _____ .

took ☐ 22 ☐ 12 years to conquer the Aztecs.

returned to Spain, where the King gave Cortez the title of _____ .

What About:

Migration

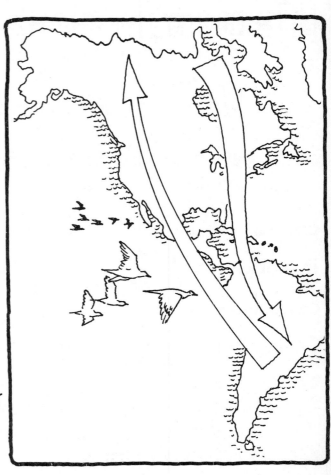

If you have seen flocks of birds flying through the air, you have probably watched migration taking place. Migration is a movement of animals looking for a better place to live. Many kinds of animals, such as insects, whales, seals, fish and birds migrate. Migration can occur on land, in water or in the air. Some animals migrate for thousands of miles. Others migrate only a few miles. Most migrating animals return to their original homes.

Many animals migrate because of weather conditions or to search for a better food supply. Often animals leave their homes in the winter and return in the spring.

One of the most fascinating migrations may be by birds. Some birds fly thousands of miles each year to find a warm home during the winter. Scientists still are puzzled by the mystery of how birds can fly so far without losing their way.

Write.

_____ is the movement of animals looking for a better place to live.

Unscramble.

What are some of the animals that migrate?

_____   _____   _____   _____   _____
s i b r d   h l w s e a   s e t n i s c   e l s s a   h i f s

Check and write.

Why do many animals migrate?

☐ Because of weather conditions
☐ Because they like winter weather
☐ To search for a better food supply

Some birds fly _____ of miles during migration.

• Draw a picture showing three kinds of migration.

Answer Key

Page 1

Ask About:

Name_____

Color Names

Did you know that there are special names that can be used to describe many colors? A dark, purplish red is called crimson. A bright red is called scarlet. Deep blue is named indigo. Emerald is a word used for bright green. Light purple is called lavender. Even white and black have unusual names! Creamy white is called ivory. Ebony is the name for deep, shiny black.

These words are often used to describe the exact way a color looks. Can you think of other special color words?

Yes or No
Many colors have special names that describe them. (Yes) No

Unscramble, write and circle each new word in the puzzle above.

ivory — yolrv — 5 3 1 4 2
scarlet — tralsec — 7 4 3 5 1 6 2
indigo — gdnoli — 5 3 2 6 1 4
emerald — mlraede — 2 6 4 5 1 7 3
lavender — danrleve — 6 2 5 8 1 4 3 7
crimson — mrscino — 4 2 5 1 3 7 6
ebony — nyboe — 4 5 2 3 1

Write.
Dark purplish red is called __crimson__.
Bright red is called __scarlet__.
Deep blue is called __indigo__.
Bright green is called __emerald__.
Light purple is called __lavender__.
Creamy white is called __ivory__.

• Draw and color a lavender dress and a scarlet umbrella.

Page 2

Ask About:

Name_____

Shapes

Shapes are all around you. Everyday things are made of different shapes. Kites can be diamond shaped. Balls, wheels and even the Earth are circles. Boxes and tables can be shaped like a square or rectangle. You can find these shapes in many common objects.

There are some unusual shapes that are harder to find in things around you. An egg is an oval. A hexagon has six sides. You can see a hexagon in some road signs. An octagon has eight sides. Can you think of something that is shaped like an octagon?

Circle.
Everyday things are made of different ships. (shapes.)

Write.

| circle |
| rectangle |
| oval |
| square |
| triangle |

triangle — rectangle — circle — oval — square

Circle.
A hexagon has four (six) sides. An octagon has (eight) six sides.

Write. hexagon   octagon

• Draw a red stop sign shaped like a hexagon.

Page 3

Ask About:

Name_____

A Diary

Do you think it would be fun to remember just what you did on a certain day two years ago? One way to remember each day is to write about it in a diary. Many people write in their diaries each day. They write about what they did, what they ate, who they saw and what they felt during that day. Most people feel very private about what they write. They do not want anyone else to read their diaries.

Long ago, many people wrote in diaries, too. Some of these old diaries have been found. They are famous because we can learn about life long ago.

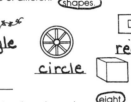

Underline.
Writing in a diary <u>is a way to remember each day.</u>
is like reading a magazine.

Check.
What do many people write about in their diaries each day?
- [x] What they did that day
- [x] Who they saw that day
- [ ] Ten math problems
- [x] How they felt about things that happened that day

Circle.
What does private mean in the story?
(People do not want anyone to read their diaries.)
People feel tired after writing in their diaries.

Write about your day in the picture diary.
• Make your own diary. Try writing every day for a week!

Page 4

Ask About:

Name_____

The Hand Calendar

Everyone knows that there are twelve months in a year. But do you have trouble remembering how many days are in each month? Some months have 31 days. Some have 30 days. Only February has 28 days.

Your hands can help you tell which are the long or short months. Make a fist with your left hand. Use your right hand to touch the knuckles and the spaces between the knuckles. As you do this, say the name of each month. When you get to the end of your hand, start back at the first knuckle. The long months will be on the knuckles. The short months will be the spaces.

January	31	February	28
March	31	April	30
May	31	June	30
July	31	August	31
September	30	October	31
November	30	December	31

Circle.
There are (twelve) twenty months in a year.

Write the month names from the picture on the lines below.

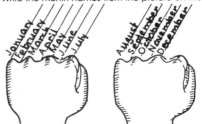

January February March April May June July   August September October November December

Knuckles = 31 days

Spaces = 30 days

(except February)

Write the number of days in each month in the circles above.
• Draw a calendar page for your birthday month.

Answer Key

Page 5

Ask About:

Name_____

The Heart

Have you ever imagined that your heart looked like a valentine? Your heart is really about the size and shape of your fist! Everytime your heart beats it pumps blood to your body. Your heart never rests. It beats 100,000 times a day!

One part of your heart sends blood to all parts of your body. The blood carries oxygen that your body needs to live. The other part of the heart takes the blood coming back from your body. It sends it to your lungs for more oxygen. Then, the fresh blood is pumped back to your body again.

Circle.
Your heart is about the size and shape of a:

valentine   (fist)

Yes or No
Your heart pumps blood through your body.   (Yes)   No
Your heart beats 25 times a day.   Yes   (No)
Your heart never rests.   (Yes)   No
Your blood carries oxygen to your body.   (Yes)   No

Underline.
Which blood has oxygen in it?
The blood which your heart sends out to the body
The blood which your heart takes back from your body

• Draw a picture which shows your heart pumping blood.

Page 5

Page 6

Ask About:

Name_____

Bones

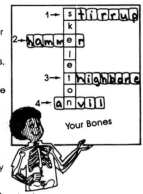

Have you ever wondered why your body has so many bones? All of the bones in your body form a skeleton. With help from your muscles and joints, the skeleton supports your body and holds it together.

Your body has 206 bones! They are different shapes and sizes. Your arms and legs have long bones. But, your toes and fingers have short bones. Your hipbone is flat. The largest bone in your body is the thighbone. It is in the top part of your leg. The smallest bones are called the hammer, anvil and stirrup. Can you guess where they are? They are in your ears!

Your Bones

Write.
All the bones in your body form a __skeleton__.
     muscle   skeleton

Check.
Your skeleton ☐ is made of skin and hair.
              ☑ supports and holds your body together.

Write.
Your body has ___206___ bones.
         How many?

Unscramble and write in puzzle.
3→The __thighbone__ is the largest bone in your body.
     o h g h t I b h e
     7 2 4 8 1 3 6 5 9

The smallest bones in your body are called:
2→ __hammer__   4→ __anvil__   1→ __stirrup__
   m h e m a r   v n l l a   r p u s r t l
   3 1 5 4 2 6   3 2 4 5 1   4 7 6 1 5 2 3

• Draw a picture of your skeleton. Name as many bones as you can.

Page 6

Page 7

Ask About:

Name_____

A Rainbow

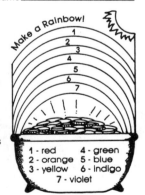

Make a Rainbow!

Have you ever seen a rainbow? A rainbow is an arch of beautiful colors. It appears in the sky when the sun shines after a rainshower. You can see a rainbow when the sun is behind you and the sky in front of you is moist from the rain.

Every rainbow has these colors: violet, indigo, blue, green, yellow, orange and red. These colors are always in the sunlight. When the sunlight shines on the raindrops, the colors separate. Each color can be seen!

You can make a rainbow by turning on a garden hose with the sun behind you. Try it!

1 - red   4 - green
2 - orange   5 - blue
3 - yellow   6 - indigo
            7 - violet

Circle.
A ~~crayon~~ (rainbow) is an arch of beautiful colors.

Underline.
When can you see a rainbow?
When the sun and rain are in front of you
When the sun is behind you and the moist air is in front of you

Write.
Name the colors of the rainbow.
r __ed__   o __range__   y __ellow__
g __reen__   b __lue__   i __ndigo__   v __iolet__

Check. ☑ These colors are always in the sunlight.
          ☐ Only children can see rainbows.
          ☑ When the sun shines on raindrops, the colors separate.
• Draw and color a rainbow.

Page 7

Page 8

Ask About:

Name_____

Clouds

Clouds

Do you like to watch clouds float by? Do you know how they are made?

The air holds water that the warm sun has pulled, or evaporated, from the earth. When this water cools in the air, it forms clouds. Clouds hold this water until they become full. Then, the water falls to the earth as rain or snow.

When a cloud is formed low along the ground, it is called fog.

Clouds are named for the way they look. Cirrus clouds are thin and high in the sky. Stratus clouds are low and thick. Cumulus clouds are white and puffy.

Cumulus
Cirrus
Stratus

Circle.
The air holds water that the warm sun has ~~burned.~~ (evaporated.)

Write.
When the water __cools__ in the air, it forms clouds.
         heats   cools

Check.
When clouds are full, the water falls to the earth as:
☐ money   ☑ snow   ☑ rain   ☐ sunshine

Write.
When a cloud is formed low on the ground, it is called __fog__
         fog   fall

Write.
A - Cirrus   Ⓒ White, puffy clouds
B - Stratus   Ⓐ Thin, high clouds
C - Cumulus   Ⓑ Low, thick clouds
Write the name of each cloud in the picture.

• Write a poem about clouds.

Page 8

Answer Key

Ask About:

Lightning

Name_____

Lightning is a flash of light caused by electricity in the sky. Clouds are made of many water droplets. All of these droplets together contain a large electrical charge. Sometimes these clouds set off a huge spark of electricity called lightning. Lightning travels very fast. As it cuts through the air, it can cause thunder.

Some lightning can look different from other lightning. Some looks like a zigzag in the sky. Sheet lightning spreads and lights the sky. Ball lightning looks like a ball of fire.

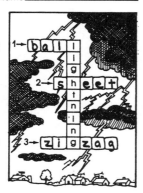

1→ **ball** lightning
2→ **sheet**
3→ **zigzag**

Underline.

Lightning is a flash of light | caused by sunshine.
<u>caused by electricity in the sky.</u>

Yes or No

Sometimes clouds set off a huge spark of electricity. (Yes) No
Lightning is caused by dry weather. Yes (No)
Lightning travels very fast. (Yes) No
Lightning can cause thunder. (Yes) No

Unscramble and write in the puzzle above.

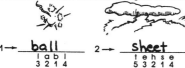

1→ **ball**
l a b l
3 2 1 4

2→ **sheet**
t e h s e
5 3 2 1 4

3→ **zigzag**
g d i z g z
3 5 2 1 6 4

• Draw a picture of a sky with the three kinds of lightning.

Page 9

Ask About:

Thunder

Name_____

Have you ever been scared by the sound of thunder? Long, long ago, people believed that thunder was the sound of angry gods in the sky. But now, scientists can tell us exactly what causes thunder.

During an electrical storm, lightning passes through the air. The air is heated by the lightning. This hot air moves out in all directions. As it does, it runs into, or collides, with cooler air. This causes a loud noise, called thunder.

Thunder can have different sounds. A loud crash comes from the main part of lightning. A low rumble means the lightning is farther away.

Check.

☐ Long ago, people believed thunder came from cracks in the earth.
☑ Long ago, people believed thunder was the sound of angry gods.

Write 1-2-3.

③ The hot air collides with cool air, causing thunder.
① Lightning heats the air as it passes through.
② The hot air moves out in all directions.

Match.

A loud crash . . . ⟍ means the lightning is farther away.
A low rumble . . . ⟋ comes from the main part of lightning.
Circle the words that tell how thunder might sound.

• Draw a picture of how people long ago felt when they heard lightning.

Page 10

Ask About:

A Tornado

Name_____

Did you know that a tornado is the most violent windstorm on Earth? A tornado is a whirling, twisting storm that is shaped like a funnel .

A tornado usually occurs in the spring on a hot day. It begins with thunderclouds and thunder. A cloud becomes very dark. The bottom of the cloud begins to twist and form a funnel. Rain and lightning begin. The funnel cloud drops from the dark storm clouds. It moves down toward the ground.

A tornado is very dangerous. It can destroy almost everything in its path.

Circle.

A (tornado) ~~thunder~~ is the most violent windstorm on Earth.

Check.

Which words describe a tornado?
☑ whirling ☑ twisting ☐ icy ☑ funnel-shaped ☑ dangerous

Underline.

A funnel shape is: ○ ▢ ⬭ <u>▽</u> ⚡

Write and Circle.

A tornado usually occurs in the **spring** on a (hot) ~~cool~~ day.

Write 1-2-3 below and in the picture above.

③ The funnel cloud drops down to the ground.
① A tornado begins with dark thunderclouds.
② The dark clouds begin to twist and form a funnel.

• Draw a dark funnel cloud.

Page 11

Ask About:

A Hurricane

Name_____

A hurricane is a powerful storm that forms over some parts of an ocean. A hurricane can be several hundred miles wide.

A hurricane has two main parts: the eye and the wall cloud. The eye is the center of the storm. In the eye, the weather is calm. The storm around the eye is called the wall cloud. It has strong winds and heavy rain. In some hurricanes, the wind can blow 150 miles an hour!

As the storm moves across the water, it causes giant waves in the ocean. As the storm moves over land it can cause floods, destroy buildings and kill people who have not taken shelter.

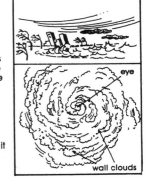
eye

wall clouds

Circle.

A hurricane has two main parts: ~~tornado~~ (wall cloud) (eye)

Write.

| wall cloud | **eye** | The calm center of the hurricane |
| eye | **wall cloud** | The wind and rainstorm around the eye |

Check:

A hurricane
☑ can be several hundred miles wide.
☑ can have winds that move 150 miles an hour.
☐ is a small storm.
☑ can cause giant waves in the ocean.
☑ can cause floods and hurt people.

• Draw a picture of the eye of a hurricane.

Page 12

Answer Key

Ask About:

A Volcano

Have you ever wondered what makes a volcano? It starts as a crack in the earth. Lava, which is hot liquid rock, comes up through the crack. When the lava comes out, it is called an eruption. When a volcano erupts, it makes a loud noise. The hot glowing lava, steam and ash pour out of the crack. As the lava cools, it gets hard. Over the years, the hard lava builds up and forms a mountain around the crack. Many volcanic mountains have taken thousands of years to form! Volcanoes do not erupt all the time. Some go for years without erupting. Some volcanoes stop erupting forever. They are called extinct.

Write.
A __volcano__ starts as a crack in the earth.
  rock   volcano

Check.
What is lava?   Dust
  ✓ Hot, liquid rock

Write 1·2·3·4.
How does a volcano form?
  ④ Over the years, the hard lava forms a mountain.
  ① A volcano starts as a crack in the earth.
  ③ The lava cools and gets hard.
  ② Lava, steam and ash pour out of the crack.

Write.
| A. extinct | __B__ Lava coming out of a volcano |
| B. eruption | __A__ A volcano that has stopped erupting |

• Draw an erupting volcano. Color the lava red.

Ask About:

Icebergs

You probably know that icebergs are huge masses of ice that are floating in parts of the oceans. But, do you know where icebergs come from?

Icebergs begin as part of ice on land, called glaciers. As the glaciers move, chunks of ice break off and fall into the ocean. These huge chunks are called icebergs.

As an iceberg floats in the water, the sun melts its top. The part underwater does not melt so quickly. So an iceberg may look small on top of the water, but still be huge underneath. This can be very dangerous for ships. The iceberg underwater can tear open a ship which passes too close!

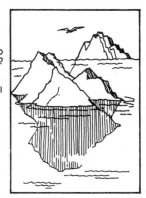

Write.
An __iceberg__ is a huge mass of ice floating in the ocean.
  island   iceberg

Circle.
Icebergs were once part of: valleys   (glaciers)   floats

Yes or No
As an iceberg floats in the water, the sun melts its top.   (Yes)   No
The iceberg underwater does not melt as quickly.   (Yes)   No
An iceberg is ice on land.   Yes   (No)

Underline.
Which part of the iceberg is larger?
  The part above the water
  The part under the water
Draw a ship passing closely to the iceberg in the ocean.

• Draw an iceberg breaking off from a glacier into the ocean.

Ask About:

Fables

A fable is a story that teaches a lesson. Most fables are short stories about animals. The animals think and talk like people. The lesson from the story is called the moral.

The most famous fables were written by Aesop hundreds of years ago. One of his fables told of a fox who tried to reach for grapes hanging on a vine above his head. He tried and tried, but he could not reach them. As he angrily went away, he said that the grapes were probably sour anyway. The moral was...a person sometimes pretends that he does not want something he cannot have!

Write.
A __fable__ is a story that teaches a lesson.
  mystery   fable

Check.

The lesson from a fable is called a
  ☐ duty.
  ☑ moral.
  ☐ lesson.

Unscramble.
__Aesop__ wrote the most famous fables.
  e A p o s
  2 1 5 4 3

Write 1·2·3 in the O's below and in the picture above.
  ② The fox could not reach the grapes.
  ① The fox tried to reach the grapes.
  ③ The fox said the grapes were probably sour anyway.

• Write your own fable.

Ask About:

Myths

Long ago, people did not understand why many things happened. They did not know why it rained, what caused lightning or how things grew. They made up stories about gods and goddesses who had special powers to make these things happen. These stories are called myths. Many of these gods and goddesses were thought to look like people. Others were thought to look like animals. Many of the gods and goddesses were said to live on mountaintops or in the sky.

People today still like to read myths from long ago. They tell how people long ago felt about the world around them.

Circle.

Long ago, people did not understand   where the Earth was.   (why things happened.)

Check.

They made up stories about
  ☑ gods.
  ☐ friends who had special powers.
  ☑ goddesses.

Write.
The gods and goddesses were thought to look like:
  __people__ or __animals__.
  party   people   lightning   animals

Circle.
Where did the gods and goddesses live?

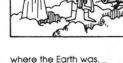
(mountain top)   hotel   (sky)

• Write a myth about why it snows.

Answer Key

Ask About: A Unicorn

Name_____

A unicorn is a mythical creature. It was said to look much like a horse, except for a large twirly horn on its forehead. The name unicorn means one horn. The unicorn stands for purity and strength. It was described as having blue eyes and a white body.

It was believed that a unicorn was pure and magical. It was thought that if a unicorn dipped its horn into a sea of poison, the water would become clear.

Everyone wanted to possess the magical horn of a unicorn. Legends say that young girls would lead unicorns to kings who would cut off the horns to gain their magical powers.

Check.
Unicorn means ☐ one horse. ☑ one horn.

Yes or No

A unicorn stands for purity and strength. ⊙Yes No
A unicorn works for kings. Yes ⊙No
A unicorn's horn was thought to be magical. ⊙Yes No

Write.
Young girls would lead unicorns to __kings__.
water kings

The kings would cut off the horns to gain __magical__ powers.
magical poison

Colors: unicorn - white   eyes - blue

• Write a poem about a unicorn.

Page 17

Ask About: Dragons

Name_____

Do you believe that dragons are real? Dragons are mythical creatures. Many countries have legends about dragons. The legends describe dragons as large lizardlike beasts that breathe fire. Most legends speak of dragons as dangerous beasts that lived in dark caves. The legends say that the dragons guarded riches found in these caves. Anyone who killed a dragon would receive the riches. These legends tell of men who killed, or slew, dragons and became heroes.

Some countries have legends about friendly dragons who stand for good luck and riches.

Check.
A dragon was said to be
☑ a lizardlike beast.
☑ a fire-breathing beast.
☐ a shy, quiet lizard.

Write.
Most legends describe dragons as __dangerous__ beasts.
dangerous lucky

The dragons were said to guard __caves__ full of riches.
cottages caves

Men who __slew__ the dragons would receive the riches.
slew caught

Circle.
In some countries, dragons stand for ⊙good luck   bad weather.   riches.

Color: dragon - green   fire - red

• Draw a dragon guarding its cave full of riches.

Page 18

Ask About: A Centaur

Name_____

A centaur is a mythical creature that was believed to be half horse and half man.

Stories of centaurs are found in myths from the country of Greece. Centaurs were thought to be cruel, wild creatures. They attacked people and animals.

But the most famous centaur, named Chiron, was not like the others. He was wise and gentle. He taught many Greek heroes about music, medicine and hunting. When he died, he became a constellation of stars in the sky. The constellation is called Sagittarius.

start

Write and Circle.
A __centaur__ was said to be ⊙half man. half cat. ⊙half horse.
centaur century

Unscramble.
The myth of the centaur comes from the country of __Greece__.
r e G c e e
2 3 1 5 4 6

Check.
Centaurs were thought to be ☑ cruel. ☐ sleepy. ☑ wild.

Yes or No
The most famous centaur was Chiron. ⊙Yes No
Chiron was wise and gentle. ⊙Yes No
Chiron taught Greek heroes many things. ⊙Yes No
Chiron was cruel and wild. Yes ⊙No

Draw a line to connect the stars to make Sagittarius.

• Write a story about Chiron.

Page 19

Ask About: Minotaur

Name_____

The Minotaur was a ferocious, mythical beast that lived on the island of Crete. It was said to have the body of a man and the head of a bull.

The legend tells that the Minotaur was locked up in a great maze under the palace of the wicked King Minos. The king would send people into the maze for the Minotaur to kill.

Theseus, the son of a good king, fell in love with King Minos' daughter. He went into the maze and killed the evil Minotaur. He found his way out of the maze by following a trail of woolen string he had unrolled on his way into the maze!

Maze ?

Unscramble.
The __Minotaur__ was a mythical beast on the island of Crete.
t l o M n r u a
5 2 4 1 3 8 7 6

Match.
The Minotaur had the:
body of a ⨉ bull
head of a ⨉ man

Write.
King Minos kept the Minotaur in a __maze__.
palace maze

Check.
☑ Theseus fell in love with the daughter of King Minos.
☐ The Minotaur killed King Minos.
☑ Theseus killed the Minotaur.
☑ Theseus followed a trail of string to get out of the maze.

Draw a line through the maze from Theseus to the Minotaur.

• Make up your own maze.

Page 20

Answer Key

Ask About: Mermaids

Name_____

Do you believe in mermaids? A mermaid is a mythical creature. Through the years people have written about a sea creature which is said to be half woman and half fish. Mermaids are described as having long, golden hair and beautiful singing voices.

Mermaids are said to sit on rocks and comb their long hair. When they see a man, they put a cap on his head. The cap is thought to be magic. It allows the person wearing it to live underwater with the mermaid.

If you swim in the ocean, perhaps you will see a mermaid!

Write.
A mermaid is a __mythical__ creature.
<u>desert</u>   <u>mythical</u>

Check.
What is a mermaid said to look like?
☑ half woman   ☑ half fish   ☐ 4 legs   ☑ long, golden hair

Circle.

I sit on a (rock) step and comb my (hair) voice.
I have a beautiful (singing) swimming voice.
I have a (magical) mirror cap that I put on a man.

Draw a mermaid in the water.

• Write a story about meeting a mermaid.

Page 21

Ask About: The Abominable Snowman

Name_____

The abominable snowman is a creature that some people believe lives on the highest mountain in the world, Mount Everest.

The abominable snowman is called Yeti. It is thought to be a huge, hairy animal with a body like an ape and a head much like a human. It is believed that Yeti comes down from the mountain and attacks the people and animals in the villages.

Some people believe that is is just a bear or gorilla. Others believe that high in the mountains is a real Yeti! What do you think?

Yes or No
Some people believe that an abominable snowman really exists. (Yes) No
They believe the snowman lives on Mount Everest. (Yes) No
They believe the snowman is made of snow and ice. Yes (No)
Mount Everest is the highest mountain in the world. (Yes) No

Unscramble.
The abominable snowman is called __Yeti__.
e i Y t
2 4 1 3

Match.
Yeti is thought to have a:
hairy body .... much like a human.
head .... like an ape.

Color Yeti brown.

• Draw a picture of where you think Yeti would live in the mountains.

Page 22

Ask About: The Loch Ness Monster

Name_____

Nessie

Do you know about one of the most famous monsters in the world? It is the Loch Ness Monster. It is a large animal that some people believe lives in Loch Ness, a deep dark lake in Scotland. For many years, hundreds of people have reported seeing something strange in the lake. They have even given it a nickname— "Nessie"!

Nessie is said to be about 30 feet long, with a long slender neck, one or two humps and flippers.

There are even pictures which have been taken of a large animal-like shape in the water. Scientists are still trying to solve the mystery of Nessie!

Circle and Write in Puzzle.
1→ Where is the Loch Ness Lake?
(Scotland) Highland
2→ It is famous for the Loch Ness...
people (Monster)
3→ What is the monster's nickname?
Nellie (Nessie)

1→ S c o t l a n d
2→ M o n s t e r
3→ N e s s i e

Check.
How has Nessie been described?
☑ about 30 feet long   ☐ 8 legs
☑ long neck   ☑ 1 or 2 humps

Write.
Hundreds of people have __reported__ seeing Nessie.
<u>studied</u>   <u>reported</u>

Draw a picture of how you think Nessie would look under the water.

• Write a story of how you would look for Nessie!

Page 23

Ask About: Atlantis

Name_____

Have you ever heard of the lost continent of Atlantis? Legend says that Atlantis was a great island in the Atlantic Ocean. Earthquakes and floods shook Atlantis and sank it.

Over the years, countries have sent ships sailing the ocean looking for Atlantis.

The story of Atlantis was first told by a famous Greek named Plato. Later, his tale fascinated many people. Explorers sailing the ocean thought they had found Atlantis many times. They were really finding the many islands that lie in the Atlantic Ocean.

Unscramble and Circle.
Legend says that __Atlantis__ was an island in the (Atlantic) Pacific Ocean.
t n l A a l s t
2 5 7 1 4 3 8 6

Write.
__Earthquakes__ and __floods__ shook and sank Atlantis.
<u>Tornadoes</u> <u>Earthquakes</u>   <u>snow</u> <u>floods</u>

Check.
The story of Atlantis was first told by
___ explorers.
✓ Plato.

Yes or No
Countries have sent ships looking for Atlantis. (Yes) No
Some explorers thought they had found Atlantis. (Yes) No
Atlantis is a nice vacation island. Yes (No)
Explorers were finding other islands in the Atlantic Ocean. (Yes) No

• Draw a picture of how you believe Atlantis would have looked.

Page 24

Answer Key

Page 25

Ask About:

Pompeii

Almost 2000 years ago, Pompeii was a rich and beautiful city in the Bay of Naples. The city lay close to a great volcano Mount Vesuvius.

One day, Vesuvius began to rumble and erupt. Lava, steam and ash burst from the volcano. Soon the sky was black with ash. The ash rained down on Pompeii. The people tried to hide in buildings or escape to the sea in boats. But, the ash fell so quickly that people were buried wherever they were. The city was covered with over twelve feet of ash!

In recent years, scientists have found Pompeii. Much of its contents were just as they were the day Mount Vesuvius erupted.

Unscramble.

__Pompeii__ was once a city in the Bay of Naples.
o e l P m p i
2 5 6 1 3 4 7

Circle.
Pompeii lay close to ~~Mount Everest,~~ (Mount Vesuvius,) a great volcano.

Write 1-2-3-4.
What happened when Vesuvius erupted?
③ People tried to hide or escape in boats.
① Mount Vesuvius began to rumble and erupt.
④ The city was buried in the ash.
② Ash began raining down on the city.

• Draw a picture of how you think Pompeii looked when it was found.

Page 25

Page 26

Ask About:

A UFO

Have you ever seen a UFO? A UFO is an Unidentified Flying Object. A UFO is a strange object or light that people see in the sky. Many people believe that these strange lights are really spaceships from another planet.

For years, people have seen and heard many odd things in the sky: blinking and glowing lights, flying objects shaped like saucers and moving objects making strange noises. Some people have even taken pictures of these unusual sights.

Some of these UFO's are really airplanes, weather balloons or meteors. But, many UFO reports are still a mystery!

Write (see story).
What does UFO stand for?
U __nidentified__   F __lying__   O __bject__

Circle.
Many people believe these UFO's are ~~airplanes~~ (spaceships) from other planets.

Check.
What odd things have people reported seeing or hearing?
☑ Blinking and glowing lights
☑ Saucer-shaped flying objects
☐ Large, red parachutes
☑ Moving objects making strange noises

Circle.
Some UFO's are really:
(airplanes)   (weather balloons)   kites   (meteors)

• Write a story about a UFO.

Page 26

Page 27

Ask About:

The Solar System

Our solar system is made up of the sun and all the objects that go around, or orbit, the sun.

The sun is the only star in our solar system. It gives heat and light to the nine planets in the solar system. The planets and their moons all orbit the sun.

The time it takes for each planet to orbit the sun is called a year. A year on Earth is 365 days. Planets closer to the sun have shorter years. Their orbit is shorter. Planets farther from the sun take longer to orbit, so their years are longer. A year on Pluto is 248 of our years!

Asteroids, comets and meteors are also part of our solar system.

Draw the nine planets around the sun.

Underline.
The solar system is: the sun without the nine planets.
__the sun and all the objects that orbit the sun.__

Check.
The Sun
☑ is the center of our solar system.
☑ is the only star in our solar system.
☐ is a planet in our solar system.
☑ gives heat and light to our solar system.

Write.
A __year__ is the time it takes for a planet to orbit the sun.
month   year

Match.
Planets closer to the sun . . .⟍⟋have a longer year.
Planets farther from the sun . . .⟋⟍have a shorter year.

• Draw and color a picture of our solar system.

Page 27

Page 28

Ask About:

Mercury

Mercury is the smallest of the nine planets in our solar system. It is also the nearest planet to the sun.

Mercury spins very slowly. The side next to the sun gets very hot before it turns away from the sun. The other side freezes while away from the sun. As the planet slowly spins, the frozen side then becomes burning hot and the hot side becomes freezing cold.

Even though Mercury spins slowly, it moves around the sun very quickly. That is why it was named Mercury— after the Roman messenger for the gods.

Color Mercury's:
hot side - red
cold side - blue

Underline.
Mercury   is the largest planet in our solar system.
__is the smallest planet in our solar system.__

Write.
Mercury is the __nearest__ planet to the sun.
darkest   nearest

Match.
How does spinning slowly affect the temperature on Mercury?
The side next to the sun ⟍⟋ is freezing cold.
The side away from the sun ⟋⟍ is burning hot.

Circle.
Mercury moves (quickly) around the sun. Mercury spins very ~~lightly.~~ (slowly.)
quietly

Check.
Mercury was named for the ☐ famous Roman speaker.
☑ Roman messenger for the gods.

• Find out more about Mercury, the Roman messenger for the gods.

Page 28

Answer Key

Ask About: Venus

Name_____

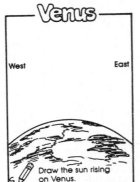

Venus is the nearest planet to Earth. Because it is the easiest planet to see in the sky, it has been called the Morning Star and Evening Star. The Romans named Venus after their goddess of love and beauty.

Venus is covered with thick clouds. The sun's heat is trapped by the clouds. The temperature on Venus is nearly 900 degrees!

Space probes have been sent to study Venus. They have reported information to scientists. But they can only last a few hours on Venus because of the high temperature.

Venus turns in the opposite direction from Earth. So, on Venus, the sun rises in the west and sets in the east!

Venus
West   East

Draw the sun rising on Venus.

Unscramble and Circle.

__Venus__ is the (nearest) planet to Earth.
  e s V u n   friendliest
  2 5 1 4 3

Check.
It is called the
☐ Evening Sun
☑ Morning Star because it is so easy to see.
☑ Evening Star

Circle.
The Romans named Venus for their:
(goddess of love and beauty)   god of light   goddess of truth

Yes or No
Half of Venus is frozen with ice and snow.   Yes (No)
Space probes have reported information from Venus.   (Yes) No
On Venus, the sun rises in the east and sets in the west.   Yes (No)

• Draw a picture of what a space probe would see on Venus.

Page 29

Ask About: Mars

Name_____

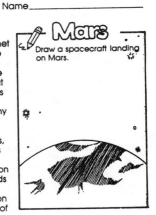
Draw a spacecraft landing on Mars.

Mars is often called the Red Planet because it looks like a red star in the night sky.

Mars is the fourth planet from the sun. It is only half the size of Earth. But since it has no oceans or lakes, it has as much land as Earth. There is no rainfall on Mars. The planet has many large deserts with huge dust storms that cover the entire planet.

Mars has seasons much like Earth's, but they last twice as long. Mars has two small moons.

Robot spacecraft have landed on Mars. They have sent back thousands of pictures. These pictures show volcanoes, canyons and channels on Mars. But, so far, they show no signs of life on Mars.

Check.
☑ Mars looks like a red star in the night sky.
☑ Mars is the fourth planet from the sun.
☐ Mars is twice the size of Earth.
☑ Mars has two small moons.
☑ Mars has longer seasons than Earth.

Unscramble.
Mars is often called the __Red__ __Planet__.
                        e R d   e n P t a l
                        2 1 3   5 4 1 6 3 2

Circle.
What would you find on Mars?
rain   ocean   (canyon)   (channel)   lake   (volcano)   (dust)

• Write a story about what you would like to find on Mars.

Page 30

Ask About: Jupiter

Name_____

Jupiter is the largest planet in our solar system. It has sixteen moons. Jupiter is the second brightest planet—only Venus is brighter.

Jupiter is bigger and heavier than all of the other planets together. It is covered with thick clouds. Many loose rocks and dust particles form a ring around Jupiter.

One of the most fascinating things about Jupiter is its Great Red Spot. The Great Red Spot of Jupiter is a huge storm in the atmosphere. It looks like a red ball. This giant storm is larger than Earth! Every six days it goes completely around Jupiter.

Jupiter
3→ clouds
5→ spot
4→ sixteen
2→ sixteen
1→ largest

Color the Great Red Spot circling Jupiter.

Unscramble and write in puzzle.

1→ Jupiter is the __largest__ planet in our solar system. 2→ Jupiter
           e t s l r g a
           5 7 6 1 3 4 2

has __sixteen__ moons. 3→ Jupiter is covered with thick
     t n x s e l e
     4 7 3 1 5 2 6

__clouds__. 4→ Loose rocks and dust form a __ring__ around
  d s o c l u   g i r h
  5 6 3 1 2 4   4 2 1 3

Jupiter. 5→ The Great Red __Spot__ of Jupiter is a huge storm.
                           t S o p
                           4 1 3 2

Circle and Write.

Jupiter is the second (brightest) planet.
                       largest

Jupiter is __bigger__ and (heavier) than all planets together.
           bigger   lighter
           redder

• Draw Jupiter, its sixteen moons and the Great Red Spot.

Page 31

Ask About: Saturn

Name_____

Saturn is probably most famous for its rings. The rings which circle Saturn are made of billions of tiny pieces of ice and dust. Although these rings are very wide, they are very thin. If you look at the rings from the side, they are almost too thin to be seen.

Saturn is the second largest planet in our solar system. It is so big that 758 Earths could fit inside it!

Saturn is covered by clouds. Strong, fast winds move the clouds quickly across the planet.

Saturn has 22 moons! Its largest moon is called Titan.

Draw 22 moons around Saturn!

Circle.
Saturn is most famous for its   spots.   (rings.)

Write.
Saturn's rings are made of __ice__ and __dust__.
                         mud ice   dust moons

Check.
Saturn's rings are
☐ red, yellow and purple.
☑ wide, but thin.

Underline.
Saturn... is the second largest planet in our solar system.
is big enough to hold 758 Earths inside it.
is farther from the sun than any other planet.
is covered by fast, strong winds.
has 22 moons.

Unscramble.
Saturn's largest moon is called __Titan__.
                                i T a n t
                                2 1 4 5 3

• Color Saturn's rings blue.

Page 32

Answer Key

Ask About:

Uranus

Did you know that Uranus was first thought to be a comet? Many scientists studied the mystery "comet." It was soon decided that Uranus was a planet. It was the first planet to be discovered through a telescope.

Scientists believe that Uranus is made of rock and metal with gas and ice surrounding it.

Even through a telescope, Uranus is not easy to see. That is because it is almost two billion miles from the sun that lights it. It takes Uranus 84 Earth years to orbit the sun!

Scientists know that Uranus has five moons and is circled by nine thin rings. But there are still many mysteries about this faraway planet.

Uranus

✏️ Draw nine thin rings around Uranus.

Circle.

Uranus was first thought to be a moon. (comet.)

Write.

Uranus was the first planet to be discovered through a __telescope__
telescope   TV

Check.

Scientists believe that Uranus is made of:

☑ rock ☐ oil ☑ metal ☐ oceans ☑ gas ☑ ice

Match.

two billion miles — . . .the number of Uranus' moons
84 Earth years — . . .the distance of Uranus from the sun
five — . . .the number of Uranus' rings
nine — . . .the time it takes Uranus to orbit the sun

• Draw a telescope that could be used to view Uranus.

Ask About:

Neptune

Neptune is the eighth planet from the sun. It is difficult to see Neptune—even through a telescope. It is almost three billion miles from Earth.

Scientists believe that Neptune is much like Uranus—made of rock, iron, ice and gases.

Neptune has two moons. Scientists believe that it may also have rings.

Neptune is so far away from the sun that it takes 164 Earth years for it to orbit the sun just once!

Neptune is a cold and distant planet that scientists still know very little about.

Neptune

✏️ Draw 2 moons around Neptune.

Write, Circle or Unscramble.

N eptune is the sixth planet from the sun.
(eighth)

E arth is almost three __billion__ miles from Neptune.
million   billion

P eople know (very little) about Neptune.
very much

T elescopes are used to see Neptune. (Yes) No

U ranus and Neptune are made of: (rock) soap (gases) (ice)

N eptune is a __cold__ and __distant__ planet.
warm cold   distant near

E very orbit around the __sun__ takes Neptune 164 Earth years.
u s n
2 1 3

• Find out how Neptune got its name.

Ask About:

Pluto

Pluto is the ninth planet from the sun. It is farther from the sun than any other planet.

If you stood on Pluto, the sun would look just like a bright star in the sky. Pluto is so far away that it gets little of the sun's heat. That is why it is freezing cold on Pluto.

Some scientists think that Pluto was once one of Neptune's moons that escaped from orbit and drifted into space. Other scientists believe it has always been a planet in our solar system.

Pluto is so far away from the sun that it takes 247 Earth years just to orbit the sun once!

Pluto

✏️ Draw how the sun would look from Pluto.

Unscramble and Circle.

__Pluto__ is the seventh planet from the sun.
l t P o u   (ninth)
2 4 1 5 3

Pluto is (farther) from the __sun__ than any other planet.
closest   n u s
                  3 2 1

Check.

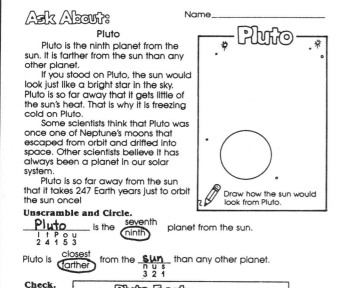

Pluto Facts

☑ On Pluto, the sun looks like a bright star.
☑ Pluto gets very little of the sun's heat.
☐ Pluto has very hot weather.
☑ Pluto takes 247 Earth years to orbit the sun.

Circle.

Some scientists believe that Pluto was once Neptune's sun, (moon)

• Write a story about what you would find on Pluto.

Ask About:

Constellations

On a clear night, you can see about two thousand stars in the sky. Scientists can use giant telescopes to see billions of stars.

Stars in groups form pictures called constellations. These constellations have been recognized for years. Ancient people named many constellations for animals, heroes and mythical creatures. Many of these names are still used.

Some constellations can be seen every night of the year. Others change with the seasons.

Since all stars are constantly moving, these same constellations that we now see will be changed thousands of years from now.

Little Dipper

✏️ Connect the stars to form the constellation called the Little Dipper.

Write.

Stars in groups form pictures called __constellations__.
telescopes   constellations

Check.

Ancient people named many constellations for:

☑ animals ☑ heroes ☐ oceans ☑ mythical creatures

Match.

Billions of stars can be seen.
About two thousand stars can be seen.

Yes or No

Some constellations can be seen every night. (Yes) No
Some constellations change with the seasons. (Yes) No
In thousands of years, all constellations will be the same. Yes (No)

• Design your own constellation. Give it a name, too.

Answer Key

Ask About:
The North Star

The North Star is one of the most famous stars. Its star name is Polaris. It is called the North Star because it shines almost directly over the North Pole.

Because the North Star is always in the same spot in the sky, it has been used for years to give direction to people at night.

If you are at the North Pole, the North Star is directly overhead. As you travel south, the star seems lower in the sky. Only people in the Northern Hemisphere can see the North Star.

Polaris, like all stars, is always moving. Thousands of years from now, another star will get to be the North Star.

Write.

The __North__ Star is one of the most famous stars.
  Pole North

Unscramble.

__Polaris__ is the star name for the North Star.
a i o l r P s
4 6 2 3 5 1 7

Check.

☑ The North Star is almost directly over the North Pole.
☆ The North Star can be seen from anywhere in the world.
☑ The North Star can help give direction at night.
☑ Only people in the Northern Hemisphere can see the North Star.
☆ Polaris will always be the North Star.

Write the star name for the North Star on the line above.

• Draw a picture showing how the North Star helped sailors years ago.

Page 37

Ask About:
The Big Dipper

One of the most famous star patterns, or constellations, is called the Big Dipper. It is formed by seven bright stars. Three stars form the handle and four stars form the bowl. The two stars that form the outer part of the bowl always point to the North Star.

The Big Dipper is more than a picture made of stars. It can be used to tell time. That is because as the Earth moves, the Big Dipper appears to turn around the North Star once every 24 hours.

All of the stars in the Big Dipper are constantly moving. Scientists say that in several thousand years, the stars will no longer form the Big Dipper!

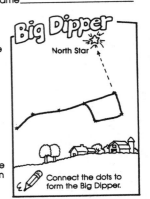

 Connect the dots to form the Big Dipper.

Circle.
One of the most famous constellations is called the:
space probe   (Big Dipper)   North Star

Check.
The Big Dipper is formed by ☐ four ☑ seven bright stars.

Match 1-2-3.
Three stars —— form the bowl.
Four stars —— form the handle.

Yes or No
Two stars in the Big Dipper point to the North Star. (Yes) No
The Big Dipper catches comets and meteors. Yes (No)
The Big Dipper will always look the same. Yes (No)

• Draw a picture of the Big Dipper.

Page 38

Ask About:
Comets

For many years, people were frightened when a comet appeared in the sky. Now we know that comets are part of our solar system. They move in an orbit around the sun.

A comet looks like a ball of fire with a long tail. When its orbit brings it closer to the sun, its tail gets much longer. This is caused by the wind and heat from the sun. Then, a comet can be 100 million miles long.

Each year new comets are discovered. Some comets can be predicted to reappear at certain times.

One of the most famous comets, Halley's Comet, reappears about once every 76 years!

Unscramble.

__Comets__ are part of our solar system.
o t s C m e
2 5 6 1 3 4

Write.

A comet looks like a ball of __fire__ with a long __tail__.
  ice fire   tail tide

Circle and write in puzzle.

1 → A comet moves in an (orbit) around the sun.
     shadow

2 → As a comet gets closer to the sun, its (tail) gets much longer.
     top

3 → One of the most famous comets is named (Halley's Comet.)
     Earth's Comet.

• Draw a comet orbiting the sun. Name your comet.

Page 39

Ask About:
A Solar Eclipse

Have you ever seen an eclipse of the sun? It is called a solar eclipse, because solar means sun. A solar eclipse happens when the sun's light is blocked from the Earth. Do you know why this happens?

The moon travels around the Earth. The Earth and the moon travel around the sun. Sometimes, the moon passes exactly between the sun and the Earth. The sun's light is blocked by the moon. The Earth becomes dark. This darkness can last from two to seven minutes. Then, as the moon moves, the sunlight appears again. A solar eclipse is an amazing event!

Check.
A solar eclipse happens . . .
☐ when the sun sets in the east.
☑ when the sun's light is blocked from the Earth.

Circle.
The word solar means: moon   Earth   (sun)

Write.

The Earth and __moon__ travel around the sun.
     sun moon

Underline.
What causes a solar eclipse?
__The moon passes between the Earth and sun and blocks the sunlight.__
The Earth does not move around the sun.

Color: Earth - blue   moon - yellow   sun - orange

• Draw a picture of the Earth during a solar eclipse.

Page 40

Answer Key

Ask About: A Black Hole

Name_____

Have you ever heard of a mysterious black hole? Some scientists believe that a black hole is an invisible object somewhere in space. The scientists believe that it has such a strong pull toward it, called gravity, that nothing can escape from it!

These scientists believe that a black hole is a star that collapsed. The collapse made its pull even stronger. It seems invisible because even its own starlight cannot escape! It is believed that anything in space that comes near the black hole will be pulled into it forever. Some scientists believe there are many black holes in our galaxy.

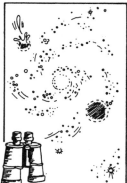

Check.
Some scientists believe that:
- ☑ a black hole is an invisible object in space.
- ☑ a black hole is a collapsed star.
- ☐ a black hole is a path to the other side of the Earth.
- ☑ a black hole has a very strong pull toward it.
- ☑ a black hole will not let its own light escape.

Write.

A - gravity
B - collapse

B To fall or cave in
A A strong pull from an object in space

Draw a spaceship being pulled into the black hole.

- Draw what you think the inside of a black hole would be like.

Page 41

Ask About: The Midnight Sun

Name_____

How would you like to live in a land where the sun shines day and night? There are places in the polar regions where, for months, the sun never sets! This is known as the Land of the Midnight Sun. This period of sunlight can last up to six months.

This happens because the Earth tilts. When the North Pole is tilted toward the sun, it has constant daylight. At that same time, the South Pole is tilted away from the sun. It is in darkness.

Six months later, the South Pole tilts to the sun and has constant daylight. Then the North Pole is tilted away. It has darkness.

Midnight Sun

Midnight

Underline.
In the land of the Midnight Sun, the sun shines every other day. <u>the sun shines for months.</u>

Write.
This sunshine can last up to <u>six</u> months.
ten   six

Circle.
The Midnight Sun happens because the Earth rests. (tilts.)

Write.

A - constant daylight
B - constant darkness

B The polar region is tilted away from the sun.
A The polar region is tilted toward the sun.

Color the Midnight Sun yellow.

- Write a story about life in the Land of the Midnight Sun.

Page 42

Ask About: The Milky Way Galaxy

Name_____

The Milky Way galaxy is made up of the Earth, its solar system and all the stars you can see at night. There are over 100 billion stars in the Milky Way!

The Milky Way is shaped much like a record. It has a center which the outer part goes around.

The Milky Way is always spinning slowly through space. It is so large that it would take 200 million years for the galaxy to turn one complete time.

Many stars in the Milky Way are in clusters. Some star clusters contain up to one million stars!

Milky Way

Our solar system
Put a red circle around our solar system.

Check.
The Milky Way galaxy is made up of
- ☑ Earth.
- ☐ no sun.
- ☑ our solar system.
- ☑ 100 billion stars.

Yes or No
The Milky Way is shaped like a pencil. Yes (No)
The Milky Way is always slowly moving in space. (Yes) No
Many stars in the Milky Way are in clusters. (Yes) No
Some star clusters have one million stars. (Yes) No

Circle.
It would take (200) 90 600 million years for the galaxy to spin once.

Underline.
Which object is the Milky Way shaped much like?

 <u>record</u>   ruler

- Write about what the Earth will be like after it circles the Milky Way one time.

Page 43

Ask About: A Planetarium

Name_____

Even though the stars in space are constantly moving, it is hard to see the changes in the sky. It takes thousands of years for some changes to be seen.

A planetarium is a special machine which shows the movements of stars and planets. It does this by placing spots of light on a curved ceiling that stands for the sky. The spots of light are made to appear and move like planets and stars. The machine can be speeded up to show thousands of years of change in just minutes. A planetarium not only can show how the sky will change in the future, but it can also show how the sky appeared thousands of years ago!

Underline.
A planetarium <u>shows the movements of stars and planets.</u>
shows the pictures of rockets.

Write 1-2-3.
How does a planetarium work?
- ② The spots appear and move like planets.
- ③ The machine can speed up to show the sky of the future.
- ① The planetarium places spots of light on a curved ceiling.

Check.
Why is a planetarium helpful?
- ☑ It lets us see how the changes in the sky occur.
- ☐ It only shows parts of the sky.

- Draw a picture of a planetarium.

Page 44

Answer Key

Page 45

Ask About:
Mammals

Did you know that you are a mammal? Mammals are warm-blooded animals. Most mammals have hair on their bodies.

Many mammals live on land. People, elephants, rabbits, dogs and cats are all land mammals.

Some mammals, like dolphins and whales, live in the water.

The seal, walrus and otter are mammals that live on land and in the water.

Did you know there is even a mammal that flies? It is the bat!

Write.
A __mammal__ is a warm-blooded animal.
reptile   mammal

Circle.
Most mammals have (hair)/scales on their bodies.

Write.

Mammals

cat   dolphin   dog   walrus   rabbit   elephant
people   seal   otter   whale

Land	Water	Land and Water
cat	dolphin	seal
people	whale	walrus
dog		otter
rabbit		
elephant		

• Write a list of ten other mammals.

Page 45

Page 46

Ask About:
Reptiles

Reptiles are a group of animals that are cold-blooded and are usually covered with scales or plates. Because reptiles are cold-blooded, they move around a lot looking for comfortable temperatures. Some reptiles even hibernate.

There are four main groups of reptiles: turtles, lizards, snakes and crocodilians. The crocodilians include alligators.

Most reptiles hatch from eggs. Young reptiles care for themselves.

Although a few snakes and lizards are poisonous, most reptiles are harmless.

Reptiles
snakes   turtles
crocodilians   lizards

Unscramble and Circle.
__Reptiles__ are (cold-blooded)/warm-blooded animals.
e R p i l e s t
2 1 3 5 6 7 8 4

Write.
Reptiles are usually covered with __scales__ or __plates__.
feathers scales   fur   plates

Circle.
There are (four)/six main groups of reptiles.

Write on the lines and in the picture above.

lizards
crocodilians
turtles
snakes

turtles   crocodilians
snakes   lizards

• Draw a picture of your favorite reptile.

Page 46

Page 47

Ask About:
Fossils

Do you ever wonder how scientists know so much about animals and plants that existed long ago? Much of their information comes from studying fossils.

A fossil is any trace found in rocks of living things from the past. Bones, shells and teeth can be fossils.

How are fossils formed? Many dinosaur fossils were formed this way: when some dinosaurs died, their bodies sank into a lake or pond and were gradually covered by mud. In time, the mud hardened into rock. The dinosaur bones inside the rock hardened, too.

People who collect and study fossils are called paleontologists.

Circle.
Scientists know much about the past from studying (fossils)/robots.

Underline.
A fossil is <u>any trace of a living thing found in rocks.</u>
a scientist's notebook.

Check.
Fossils can be: ☑bones ☐books ☑shells ☑teeth

Write 1-2-3.
How were some dinosaur fossils formed?

Color the fossil brown.
• Draw a picture of a fossil you would like to find.

Page 47

Page 48

Ask About:
The Platypus

The platypus is one of the most unusual animals in the world. The platypus lives along streams in Australia. It is a mammal, even though it lays eggs like a bird.

The platypus has a bill like a duck. That is why it is often a called a duckbilled platypus. It uses its bill to hunt for its food in streams. It eats mostly shellfish, worms and insects.

A platypus is about two feet long. It has webbed feet, which makes it an excellent swimmer.

At one time, many platypuses were killed for their fur. It is now against the law to kill a platypus.

Circle.
The platypus lives along streams in Africa./(Australia.)

Yes or No

	Yes	No
The platypus is a mammal.	(Yes)	No
The platypus lays eggs.	(Yes)	No
The platypus has a bill like a duck.	(Yes)	No
The platypus is a reptile.	Yes	(No)

Check.
The platypus eats mostly:
☑shellfish ☑worms ☐rabbits ☑insects

Circle.
The platypus is an excellent sleeper/(swimmer) because it has wide/(webbed) feet.

Underline.
It is against the law <u>to kill a platypus.</u>
to photograph a platypus.

• Write a story about a platypus.

Page 48

Answer Key

Ask About: A Piranha

Name_____

The piranha gets its name from an Indian word which means toothfish. A piranha eats mostly other fish. Piranhas are known for attacking their food and stripping it down to the bones in minutes.

Piranhas live in certain South American rivers. They usually swim in groups, or schools, of fifty or sixty. There are about twenty kinds of piranhas. Only four are known to attack large animals. The most vicious is the Black Piranha.

Piranhas will even attack each other. But they have a curious ability to heal quickly from these wounds.

Write and Circle.

Piranha is an *ancient* (Indian) word which means <u>toothfish</u>.
shark   toothfish

Unscramble.

Piranhas live in <u>South</u> <u>American</u> rivers.
S u h t o   m e n A r c a l
1 3 5 4 2   2 3 8 1 4 6 7 5

Check.
Piranhas are known for:
- [x] attacking their food and stripping it to the bones in minutes.
- [ ] attacking boats which travel on the river.

Write.
There are about <u>twenty</u> kinds of piranhas.
fifty   twenty

Circle.
The most vicious piranha is the Gold Piranha. / (Black Piranha.)

• Draw two piranhas attacking each other.

Page 49

Ask About: A Komodo Dragon

Name_____

A Komodo Dragon is not really a dragon. It is the largest living lizard in the world. A Komodo Dragon is at least ten feet long and weighs 360 pounds. It has a long tail and is covered with scales. Its mouth is lined with sharp teeth.

The Komodo Dragon gets its name from the island of Komodo in the Pacific Ocean, where most of these lizards are found. It resembles the giant dragon-like lizards that lived in prehistoric times.

The Komodo dragon hunts food in the day. At night, it hides in caves which it digs with its sharp claws.

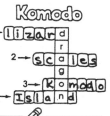

Underline.
A Komodo Dragon   is really a dragon. / <u>is really a lizard.</u>

Write in puzzle.
A Komodo Dragon:

is the largest <u>lizard</u> in the world.
1

is covered with <u>scales</u>.
2

is found on <u>Komodo</u> <u>Island</u>.
3   4

Komodo
1→ l i z a r d
        r
2→ s c a l e s
        g
3→ K o m o d o
        n
4→ I s l a n d

Match.
day ——— hides in caves
night ——— hunts for food
(lines crossed)

✎ these words:
Komodo   lizard
scales   Island

• Draw a Komodo Dragon digging its cave.

Page 50

Ask About: The Great Ice Age

Name_____

Long ago, the Great Ice Age began when the climate of Earth began to cool. As the temperature dropped, giant sheets of ice, called glaciers, moved across the land. As time went on, snow and ice covered many forests and grasslands.

Some plants and animals could not survive the changes in the climate. Other animals moved to warmer land. But some animals were able to adapt—they learned to live with the cold and snowy weather.

Finally, the Earth's temperature began to rise. The ice and snow began to melt. Today, the land at the North and South Poles is a reminder of the Great Ice Age!

Check.
The Great Ice Age
- [x] began when Earth's climate became cooler.
- [ ] began with a volcano eruption.

Write.
Sheets of ice, called <u>glaciers</u>, moved across the land.
sleet   glaciers

Circle.
Snow and ice covered many (forests) and islands. / (grasslands.)
caves

Check.
What happened to many animals?
- [x] Some animals moved to warmer land.
- [x] Some animals adapted to the colder weather.
- [ ] The colder weather did not bother the animals.
- [x] Some animals could not survive the colder weather.

• Write a story about the Great Ice Age.

Page 51

Ask About: Hibernation

Name_____

Have you ever wondered why some animals hibernate? Hibernation is a long sleep that some animals go into for the winter.

Animals get their warmth and energy from food. Some animals cannot find enough food in the winter. They must eat large amounts of food in the fall. Their bodies store this food as fat. Then in winter, they sleep in hibernation. Their bodies live on the stored fat. Since their bodies need much less food during hibernation, they can stay alive without eating new food during the winter.

Some animals that hibernate are: bats, chipmunks, bears, snakes and turtles.

Underline.
Hibernation   <u>is a sleep that some animals go into for the winter.</u>
Is the time of year to gather food for the winter.

Yes of No
Animals get their warmth and energy from food. (Yes) No
Some animals cannot find enough food in the winter. (Yes) No
Animals hibernate because they are lazy. Yes (No)
Animals need less food while they are hibernating. (Yes) No

Match.
Animals that hibernate...
eat and store food ——— in the winter.
go to sleep ——— in the fall.
(lines crossed)

Color the animals that hibernate.

• Draw a bear hibernating in a cave.

Page 52

Answer Key

Ask About:
Extinction

An animal becomes extinct when every animal of its kind has died.

One of the most famous extinct animals is the dinosaur. Some scientists believe that all of the dinosaurs died because they could not live in a changing climate.

Animals can become extinct for many reasons. Some animals have been hunted and killed. Others have been poisoned by the pollution of the land and water where they live. Some animals become extinct because people now live on the land where they once lived. The animals cannot find new places to live.

Check.
An animal becomes extinct . . .
- [ ] when it moves to a new place to live.
- [x] when every animal of its kind has died.

Circle.
One of the most famous extinct animals is the ~~shark.~~ (dinosaur.)

Why do some animals become extinct?

Some animals are __hunted__ and __killed__ .
(hunted caged) (watched killed)

Some animals are poisoned by (pollution.) ~~other animals.~~

Some animals lose their
__homes__ and cannot find new ones.
(homes help)

• Find the names of three more extinct animals.

What About:
Velcro

Many things—jackets, wallets, backpacks—have fasteners to open and close them. For years, most things were fastened with zippers, buttons, snaps and buckles. Now, Velcro has become a popular fastener.

Velcro was invented by a Swiss engineer. While camping in the woods, he noticed that burrs would stick to his clothes. Little hooks that covered the burrs would stick to loops of thread on his clothes. He decided to invent a fastener which would work like a burr. He named his product Velcro.

One piece of Velcro is made of tiny hooks—the other piece of

tiny loops. When the two pieces come together, they stick. To unfasten—just pull them apart!

List four fasteners that have been used for years:
1. **zippers** 2. **buttons** 3. **snaps** 4. **buckles**

Circle and Check.
~~Velvet~~ (Velcro) was invented by
- [ ] a Swiss surgeon.
- [x] a Swiss engineer.

Write.
Velcro was designed to work like a __burr__ .

Circle T or F.
Velcro . . . is used to fasten things. (T) F
. . . is made to work like a zipper. T (F)
. . . is made of tiny hooks and loops. (T) F
. . . has been used as long as buttons have. T (F)

Underline the sentence that tells how to unfasten Velcro.

• List 10 things that could be fastened with Velcro.

What About:
Animal Mysteries

As long as people have studied animals, there have been mysteries about why animals act certain ways.

One mystery has to do with some animals' strange behaviors before earthquakes. Horse and cattle stampedes, screeching seabirds, howling dogs, even animals coming out of hibernation early, are examples of this mysterious behavior.

Another mystery involves birds and ants. No one can explain why a bird will pick up an ant in its beak and rub the ant over its feathers again and again. This is called "anting", and birds have been known to do this for an hour without stopping.

One animal mystery is very sad. For hundreds of years, some whales have mysteriously swam from the ocean onto a beach where they would die. Reports of "beached whales" occur about five times a year somewhere in the world.

There are hundreds of other animal mysteries—such as how and why animals hibernate—that scientists have not solved. Can you think of another animal mystery?

3 Animal Mysteries

Write.
1. Some animals act strangely before an __earthquake__ .

Check.
This strange behavior includes:
- [ ] laughing birds
- [x] howling dogs
- [x] horse and cattle stampedes
- [ ] barking whales
- [x] leaving hibernation early
- [x] screeching seabirds

Write.
2. This mystery is about __birds__ rubbing __ants__ over their feathers.

Write.
3. A sad mystery is about __whales__ swimming onto a __beach__ and dying.

• Write a solution to one of the animal mysteries.

What About:
Superstitions

Have you ever avoided walking under a ladder because you thought it would bring you bad luck? If so, you were following a superstition. A superstition is a belief that if you do a certain thing it will cause a totally different thing to happen. Superstitions have existed for hundreds of years. Most people today do not believe old superstitions, but they still follow them just to be safe!

There are superstitions for almost anything people do: sleeping, working, eating, getting married, playing or just walking. There are superstitions about pets, friends, numbers, sports, weather—even the moon.

Some superstitions predict good luck—throwing rice at a bride and groom, knocking on wood, finding a four-leaf clover, or carrying a rabbit's foot. Other superstitions warn of bad luck—spilling salt, breaking a mirror, or having a black cat walk across your path. What do you think of superstitions?

Underline.
A superstition is a belief that . . .
<u>if you do a certain thing it will cause a totally different thing to happen.</u>
you will always have good luck no matter what you do.

Circle.
Most people ~~believe~~ (do not believe) in superstitions.

Check.
- [ ] Superstitions have existed for less than a hundred years.
- [x] Superstitions have existed for hundreds of years.

Unscramble.
Superstitions are thought to predict **good** or **bad** luck.
(dogo) (dba)

Underline six things in the story that superstitions can be about.

• Write a story about superstitions.

What About:

Traveling Seeds

Everyone knows that flowering plants cannot fly or run or walk. But, through their seeds, they move from place to place. That is why you can see new plants growing each year where there were none before.

Flowering plants grow in many different colors and sizes, but they all have seeds. The part of the plant which holds the seeds is called the fruit. Some seeds travel in their fruit. Others fall out and travel to a place where they can grow. But how do they get to this new place?

Some seeds stick to people's clothes or animals' fur and are carried from place to place. The seeds drop off and form new plants where they fall. Other seeds may be scattered by wind and rain. They are blown or washed to a new place where they will grow. Some seeds are not carried by people, animals, wind or rain. They are actually popped out by their own plant to grow nearby.

However it happens, seeds are constantly moving about.

Name_____

Seeds can (crossword puzzle)
- 2→ fur
- 4→ rain
- 3↓ wind
- 5↓ popped
- 1→ clothes

Write.
The part of the plant which holds the seeds is called the **fruit**.

Match. 
— Some seeds fall from their fruit before they travel.
— Some seeds travel in their fruit.

How Do Seeds Travel?

Write and circle.
Some seeds (wash / **stick**) to people's **clothes** or animals' **fur**.

Some seeds are (**scattered** / changed) by **wind** and **rain**.

Some seeds are **popped** out by their own (size / **plant**).

Write each word in the puzzle.

• Draw a picture showing the ways seeds can travel.

Page 57

What About:

Ice Cream

Almost everyone loves to eat ice cream. In fact, ice cream has been a favorite for hundreds of years. Nearly two thousand years ago, Roman rulers enjoyed eating mountain snow. In Europe, people flavored ice for a special dish. In 1295, the great explorer, Marco Polo, brought recipes from China for water ices. Later, cream was used to make ice cream much like we enjoy today.

Until 1851, ice cream was mostly made at home. Today, most ice cream is produced in ice cream plants. These plants use machines to mix milk, sugar and water. The mixture is pumped into a cooler. After it is chilled, it is put into storage tanks. Special flavors and colors are added to make many different kinds of ice cream. The mixtures are then frozen at a temperature of −22°F. Then fan-like blades slice through the frozen mixture and whip air into it. This fluffy ice cream is placed in a hardening room for 12 hours. Then off to the stores it goes!

Name_____

(crossword puzzle)
- 1→ favorite
- 2→ Europe
- 3→ Marco
- 4→ cream
- 5→ home

Unscramble, circle, write and check. Write the answers in the puzzle above.

1→ Ice cream has been a **favorite** treat for many years. (vtirfoae)

2→ In England, (**Europe**), people flavored ice for a special dish. 3→ In 1295, **Marco** Polo brought recipes from China for water ices.

4→ Later, ☐ ice / ☑ cream was used to make ice cream. 5→ Until 1851, most ice cream was made at **home**.

Write 1-6. How is ice cream made in plants?
- ② After the mixture is chilled, it is put into storage tanks.
- ④ The different mixtures are frozen at −22°F.
- ⑤ Fan-like blades slice through the mixture and whip air into it.
- ① A mixture of milk, sugar and water is pumped into a cooler.
- ③ Special colors and flavors are added.
- ⑥ The fluffy ice cream is placed in a hardening room for 12 hours.

Page 58

What About:

Insects in Winter

In the summertime, insects can be seen buzzing and fluttering around us. But as winter's cold weather begins, suddenly the insects seem to disappear. Do you know where they go?

Many insects, such as flies and mosquitoes, find a warm place to spend the winter. They live in cellars, barns, attics, caves and tree holes.

Beetles and ants try to dig deep into the ground. Some beetles stack up in piles under rocks or dead leaves.

In the fall, female grasshoppers and crickets lay their eggs and die. The eggs hatch in the spring.

Bees also try to protect themselves from the winter cold. Honeybees gather in a ball in the middle of their hive. The bees stay in this tight ball trying to stay warm.

Winter is very hard for insects, but each spring the survivors come out and the buzzing and fluttering begins again.

Name_____

Write.
When cold weather begins, **insects** seem to disappear.

Unscramble and check.
Mosquitoes (qutMsoeosi) and **flies** (sfile) find a warm place in:
☐ beds ☑ barns ☑ caves ☑ cellars ☑ attics ☐ sweaters

Circle Yes or No.
- **I**n the winter, insects look for a warm place to live. (**Yes**) No
- **N**oise, such as buzzing, can be heard all winter long. Yes (**No**)
- **S**ome beetles and ants dig deep into the ground. (**Yes**) No
- **E**very insect finds a warm home for the winter. Yes (**No**)
- **C**rickets and grasshoppers lay their eggs and die. (**Yes**) No
- **T**he honeybees gather in a ball in their hive. (**Yes**) No
- **S**urvivors of the cold weather come out each spring. (**Yes**) No

• Draw a picture showing how the insects keep warm in the winter.

Page 59

What About:

Leap Year

Do you know what leap year is and how it is different from other years? A year is measured on a calendar in months and days. The calendar year has 365 days. That is because it takes the Earth approximately 365 days to travel around the Earth. Actually, it takes the Earth 365 days, 5 hours, 48 minutes and 45 seconds to make the trip. So every year there are 5 hours, 48 minutes and 45 seconds that we don't use! To solve this problem, every four years this extra time is added up to make an extra day. The year with the extra day is called Leap Year. Leap year has 366 days. The extra day is added to the month of February. The day becomes February 29th.

Name_____

Circle.
A year is measured on a calendar in miles / (**months**) and (**days**) / pounds.

Underline.
It takes the Earth approximately 365 days...
<u>to travel around the sun.</u>
to go from winter to summer.

Write.
Exactly how long does it take the Earth to travel around the sun?
365 days **5** hours **48** minutes **45** seconds

Underline the sentence that tells how much extra time we don't use every year.

Write and check.
Every **4** years the extra time ☐ is added up to make a month. ☑ is added up to make an extra day.

Write.
The year with the extra day is called **Leap** Year.
Leap Year has **366** days.

Check.
The extra day becomes ☐ February 2nd. ☑ February 29th.

• Make a calendar page for February during Leap Year.

Page 60

Answer Key

Page 61

What About: Camouflage

A camouflage is a way of disguising or hiding something or someone. Both animals and people use camouflage to protect themselves.

Many animals have a natural camouflage. The color of their skin or fur helps them blend in with their surroundings. This lets them hide from other animals who might harm them. For example, the white polar bear lives in all the white snow and ice. Its color acts as a camouflage because the white bear is hard to see in all the white surroundings. Brown field mice and green insects have the colors of their natural homes. One animal, the chameleon, can even change colors to match its surroundings as it moves from place to place.

People have learned to use camouflage, too. Soldiers' uniforms are often earth colors so they cannot be easily seen. Warships, tanks and jeeps have been "camouflaged" with colors to match the water or land. Can you think of other camouflages?

Unscramble.
A **camouflage** is a way of disguising something or someone.
u a c o m f l g e a

T or F
animals Natural camouflage does not help animals. T (F)
Many animals have a natural camouflage. (T) F

Check.
Which are examples of natural camouflage?
- [x] A white polar bear on white snow and ice
- [ ] A red bird living in a green tree
- [x] A brown field mouse in a brown field
- [x] A green insect living in green grass

Underline the animal which can change colors to match its surroundings.

Circle.
What are some examples of camouflage that people have used?
people (soldiers' uniforms) (tanks) radios (jeeps)

• Draw three examples of camouflage for animals and people.

Page 62

What About: Hieroglyphic Writing

Can you imagine a time when people were just learning to write symbols for the words they spoke?

One of the earliest forms of writing was developed in ancient Egypt. The Egyptians used a kind of picture writing called hieroglyphics.

At first, they used simple pictures to express an idea. These pictures are called pictographs. Later, they used symbols that stood for sounds or parts of words. This picture writing is called syllabic.

Egyptians began by carving their "picture writing" on stone monuments. Later, they learned to make a paper-like material to write on. It was made from a reed plant called papyrus. The Egyptians wrote with a sharpened reed. They mixed soot and water to use as ink.

Today, some museums have examples of hieroglyphics. Language specialists can even read these ancient words.

Check and write.
One of the earliest forms of writing was developed
- [ ] in old museums. [x] in ancient Egypt.
The Egyptians used picture writing called **hieroglyphics.**

syllabic   pictographs
pictographs Simple pictures that express an idea
syllabic Symbols for sounds or parts of words

Circle.
Egyptians began by (painting (carving)) pictures (on their houses. (on stone monuments))

Write T or F.
Egyptians... T made "paper" from a papyrus plant.
F wrote with pencils and pens.
T made "ink" from soot and water.

• Make up your own hieroglyphic writing.

Page 63

What About: A Boomerang

Have you ever thrown a boomerang to see if it would spin back to you?

Boomerangs are flat, curved objects that can be thrown for fun or as a sport. But scientists believe that the first boomerangs were made by cavemen and used as weapons.

There are really two kinds of boomerangs—returning and non-returning. A returning boomerang is made to spin through the air in a curve and return to the thrower. It is used mostly for fun or as a sport. The cavemen made non-returning boomerangs. These boomerangs were thrown in a straight path. They were a valuable hunting weapon because they could spin through the air and hit a target harder than a stick or stone could.

Boomerangs were considered so important that they were often decorated and used in ceremonies.

Write and Circle.
A **boomerang** is a flat, (curved straight) object that can be thrown.
o r g b o e n a m

Check.
Scientists believe that cavemen
- [x] made the first boomerangs.
- [x] used boomerangs as weapons.
- [ ] used boomerangs for cooking.

Write.
The two kinds of boomerangs are **returning** and **non-returning.**
A   B

Write A or B.
B Spins through the air in a straight path
A Spins through the air and returns to the thrower
B Was a valuable hunting weapon for cavemen
A Is used mostly for fun or as a sport

Underline the sentence that tells why the boomerang was a valuable weapon.

• Draw a picture showing how boomerangs have been used.

Page 64

What About: Quicksand

Many stories of people and animals sinking into quicksand have been told for hundreds of years. Although some of the stories may be true, it helps to understand what quicksand really is.

Quicksand is a deep bed of light, loose sand that is full of water. On the surface it looks much like regular sand, but it is really very different. Regular sand is packed firmly and can be walked on. Because quicksand is loose and full of water, it cannot support much weight.

Quicksand usually develops around rivers and lakes. Water collects in the sand and does not drain away. It continues to collect until the sand becomes soft.

Although some objects can float in quicksand, it cannot support the heavy weight of an animal or person.

Check and write.
Quicksand is a bed of [x] light [ ] dry [x] loose sand that is full of **water.**

Match.
Regular sand ✗ is loose and full of water.
Quicksand ✗ is packed firmly and can be walked on.

Check.
Quicksand
- [ ] usually develops in the deserts.
- [x] usually develops around rivers and lakes.
- [x] cannot support the heavy weight of an animal or person.

True or False
How does quicksand develop?
T Water collects in the sand and the sand becomes soft.
F Water is drained from the sand and the sand becomes firm.

• Draw a picture showing how quicksand is formed.

Answer Key

What About:

Totem Poles

Totem poles are fascinating to see. They are carved or painted poles featuring people and animals. These carvings are symbols which stand for certain families or tribes. Many totem poles were made by North American Indians to represent the various tribes. Some tribes used birds, fish or animals as their symbols. These symbols are called totems. Many tribes once believed their totems were sacred. Some tribes prayed to their totems. Tribes even took the names of their totems as their tribal names. Often, there were

laws against killing the animals which were chosen as totems.

A totem pole was carved to show the symbol, or totem, for a tribe. Totem poles were displayed with pride. Often a tribe would have a feast, called a potlatch, to celebrate a new totem pole.

Underline.
Totem poles show. . .
<u>symbols which stand for certain families or tribes.</u>
symbols which stand for famous hunters.

Write.
Many totem poles were made by **North American** Indians.

Check.
Some tribes used these as their symbols:
☑ birds ☐ smoke ☑ fish ☐ arrows ☑ animals

Unscramble.
A tribe's symbol is called a **totem.**
_e o t t m_

True or False
T Many tribes believed their totems were sacred.
F Some tribes thought their children were totems.
T Some tribes prayed to their totems.
T Some tribes took their totem's name as their tribal name.

• Design your own totem pole. Write a paragraph about its meaning.

What About:

Galapagos Islands

One of the most fascinating places in the world is the Galapagos Islands, located in the Pacific Ocean just along the equator. The islands lie 650 miles west of Ecuador, a country in South America. The Galapagos Islands, which are made up of fifteen islands, are covered with volcanic peaks.

The islands are famous for several reasons. Long ago, pirates buried their treasures on the islands. The islands were called the Enchanted Islands. But the Galapagos Islands are most famous for the unusual animals and birds which live there. Many

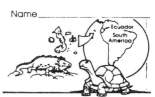

of these animals are not found anywhere else in the world. Living on the island are birds that cannot fly, giant turtles that weigh 500 pounds and penguins which are normally only found in the Antarctic. <u>But the most incredible sight on the Galapagos Islands may be the huge lizards, called iguanas.</u> The iguanas often grow to be four feet long!

Check.
The islands are most famous for ☐ their unusual sunsets.
☑ their unusual animals and birds.

Write, circle and check.
The Galapagos Islands... are covered with **volcanic** peaks.
lie ⑥⑤ ⓞ miles west of **Ecuador**
are made up of ☐ fifty ☑ fifteen islands.
are located in the **Pacific** Ocean along the Arctic. ⓔquator.

Match.
Living on the islands are. . .
birds ⤬ that weigh 500 pounds.
giant turtles ⤬ that grow to be four feet long.
penguins ⤬ that cannot fly.
lizards — normally only found in the Antarctic.
Underline the sentence that gives a name for the huge lizards.

• Write about what you might find on the Galapagos Islands.

What About:

Stonehenge.

Stonehenge is an ancient monument made of a group of huge stones. It is located in Wiltshire, England. It is not known who put them there or what they really mean. Some scientists believe that they were put there thousands of years ago by people who worshipped the sun.

Through the years, many of the original stones fell or were carried away and used to build other things. But many stones still stand in place. From these stones and other markings, scientists believe they know how the monument looked when it was first built. They believe that it

was a circle of large stones with other stones in the center. These center stones were probably used as an altar. Some scientists believe that Stonehenge was built by ancient people to study the sun. They may have used the monument to predict changes in the seasons—even eclipses of the sun!

Check.
Stonehenge
☑ is an ancient monument made of a group of huge stones.
☑ is located in Wiltshire, England.
☐ was built as a place to study the ocean.

Circle.
Stonehenge may have been built ⟨thousands⟩ hundreds of years ago.

Underline.
Some scientists believe that Stonehenge . . .
may have been built as a castle.
<u>may have been built by sun worshippers.</u>

True or False
T Over the years, many of the stones fell or were carried away.
F Only five stones remain as a monument.
F The center stones were probably used as a house.
T Ancient people may have used the monument to study the sun.

• Draw a picture showing how the ancient people used Stonehenge.

What About:

Castles

Over a thousand years ago, Europe was living in a time of lords, knights and many wars. This time is called the Middle Ages or the Medieval Period.

During this time, the wealthy lords lived in castles. A castle was a huge building that was often surrounded by a stone wall. But a castle was more than just a home. Because of the many wars, a lord used his castle as a place to protect his family and friends.

Castles had many kinds of rooms. The lord and his family lived in the center of the castle, known as the keep. The keep had sleeping rooms, dining rooms, praying rooms and

kitchens. There were rooms for swords and other weapons, and, of course, a dungeon where prisoners were kept.

Outside, there were watchtowers, gardens and stables. Many castles were surrounded by a moat. A moat was a large, deep ditch filled with water. The moat helped protect the castle. A drawbridge was used to let people go in and out of the castle.

Today in Europe, many of the castles still stand much as they did in the Middle Ages!

Circle.
The keep had rooms for boats ⟨swords⟩ and other weapons.

Write and check.
Over a thousand years ago, Europe was living in a time that we call **Middle** Ages or **Medieval** Period.
This was a time of: ☑ lords ☑ knights ☐ peace ☑ many wars
During the Middle Ages, lords lived in **castles.**

Check.
Outside, there were: ☑ watchtowers ☑ stables
☑ gardens ☐ kitchens

Circle.
Many castles were surrounded by a large ditch called a ⟨moat.⟩ river.

Write.
People were able to cross the moat on a **drawbridge.**

• Write a story about life in a castle.

Answer Key

What About: Braille

Have you ever seen a book that is written in braille? Braille is a special system that makes it possible for blind people to read. It is made by a code of dots raised on the paper. A blind person can then read the code by touching the dots.

Braille was developed in 1829 by Louis Braille, a 15-year-old blind student in France. His code is still used today.

Braille is made from six dots. The dots are placed two across, and three down. From these six dots, many different symbols can be made by raising certain dots. This six-dot code can make the alphabet, numerals, punctuation marks and more.

Braille material is made by a process that puts the dotted code on metal plates. The plates are then pressed against paper. This forms the dotted code on the paper. Books, magazines and even menus are written in braille.

Check.

Braille ☑ is a special system that allows blind people to read.
☐ is a code used to send secret messages.

True or False

T Braille is made by a code of dots raised on the paper.
T Braille is read by touching the dots.
T Braille was developed by a blind student.
F Braille was developed in Italy in 1829.

Write.
How many dots are used to make the Braille code? six

Write 1, 2, 3.
How is braille made?
② The metal plates are pressed against paper.
① The dotted code is put on metal plates.
③ The dotted code is formed on the paper.

• Write a story of how you think the braille code was developed.

What About: Hearing Aids

A hearing aid is a wonderful invention that helps improve a person's hearing. There are two basic kinds of hearing aids: air conduction aids and bone conduction aids. The air conduction aid increases the sound and brings it directly into the ear. The bone conduction aid brings the sound waves to the bones behind the ear. The sound vibrations move through the bones into the ear.

People have used "hearing aids" for hundreds of years. One of the first aids was the ear trumpet, which looked like a large funnel. People would hold the ear trumpet to their ear to help them hear.

Alexander Graham Bell tried to make a hearing aid. He was unsuccessful, but his work helped him invent something else—the telephone! But his work helped others. In 1902, the first battery-powered hearing aid was invented.

Today, hearing aids use transistors or tiny batteries. This makes hearing aids much smaller and easier to use. Hearing aids can even be made in the earpiece of eyeglasses!

Write.
What are the two basic kinds of hearing aids?
air conduction aids   bone conduction aids

Write and check.
One of the first hearing aids was called an ear trumpet.

The ear trumpet was shaped like a ☐ bell.
☑ funnel.

T or F
Alexander Graham Bell invented the first hearing aid. T (F)
In 1902, the first battery-powered hearing aid was invented. (T) F
Hearing aids can be made in the earpiece of eyeglasses. (T) F

Circle.
Modern hearing aids use (trumpet/transistors) or (batteries)/funnels.

• Draw a picture showing how the two kinds of hearing aids work.

What About: Eyeglasses

Many people wear eyeglasses to improve their eyesight. Eyeglasses are made with two lenses held together by a frame. Eyeglasses are made in many colors, shapes and sizes.

Eyeglasses may have first been made in Italy in the 1200's. These early glasses were worn by balancing them on the nose! These first glasses probably did little to improve eyesight.

It wasn't until the 1700's that eyeglasses were made which greatly improved eyesight. These glasses were set in frames which had sidepieces that rested on the ears.

Eyeglasses can help people in different ways. Some people cannot see things far away. This is called nearsightedness. Some people cannot see things close to them. This is called farsightedness. Glasses can be worn to correct both problems.

Some people need help seeing things both far and near. Glasses, called bifocals, are made to correct this problem. Bifocals were invented by an American, Benjamin Franklin.

Crossword answers:
1 → eyesight
3 → Italy
2 → lenses
4 → greatly
10 → Franklin
5 → ears
6 → nearsightedness
7 → farsightedness
8 → near
9 → bifocals

Write.
Many people wear glasses to improve their eyesight.
Eyeglasses are made with two ²lenses held together by a frame.
Eyeglasses may have first been made in ³Italy.
Eyeglasses in the 1700's ⁴greatly improved eyesight.
These had frames with sidepieces that rested on the ⁵ears.
⁶Nearsightedness when people cannot see things far away
⁷Farsightedness when people cannot see things close to them
Some people need help seeing both far and near ⁸near.
Special glasses, ⁹bifocals, help people see both far and near.
Bifocals were invented by Benjamin ¹⁰Franklin.

What About: Sound

It is easy to take all of the sounds around us for granted. But do you really know what sound is? Sound is caused by something quivering back and forth. This quivering motion is called a vibration. Vibrations travel through the air. You hear them as sounds. The air can carry many vibrations at one time. This is how you can hear many sounds at the same time. Different sounds are created according to how fast something vibrates. The faster it vibrates, the higher the sound. A slower vibration causes a lower sound.

Some unpleasant sounds are called noise. Noise can be harmful to your hearing. Loud

noises, such as airplanes or machines, can even cause a hearing loss. But other sounds, such as (music) or (talking,) are not dangerous—just pleasant!

Unscramble.
Sound is caused by something quivering back and forth.
o d S n u

Check.
Vibrations ☑ travel through the air.
☑ are heard as sounds.
☐ travel through the air one at a time.

Underline.
Different sounds are made by
how hot the air becomes.
how fast something vibrates.

Match.
The faster something vibrates . . . ⟍ the lower the sound.
The slower something vibrates . . . ⟋ the higher the sound.

Write.
Some unpleasant sounds are noise. Underline two examples of harmful noise. Circle two examples of pleasant sounds.

• List five pleasant sounds and five noises.

Answer Key

What About: Ballet

Name_____

Ballet is one of the most unusual and beautiful dances ever performed. A ballet dancer must be very strong and coordinated to do many of the spins, leaps and turns. But ballet dancers must also be graceful. This allows them to make the difficult moves look easy.

Ballet is for men and women. The women often dance on the tips of their toes.

Ballet began in Italy in the 1400's. The first ballet told stories in dance. The dancers wore fancy costumes. Many of their dances told of Greek myths and legends. This ballet was very

different from today's ballet.

Today's ballet is called classical ballet. It was first developed in France during the 1600's. Special steps and positions made this ballet different from any before. Today's dancers still use the French names for each of these steps and positions.

Unscramble and circle.

__Ballet__ is one of the easiest ways to exercise.
(IBealt)   most unusual dances ever performed.

Circle and check.

A ballet dancer must be very ~~short~~ (strong) and coordinated to do the:

☑ spins ☐ cartwheels ☑ leaps ☐ jumping jacks ☐ spine

True or False

The first ballet
. . . began in Italy in the 1400's (T) F
. . . dancers told stories in songs. T (F)
. . . told of Greek myths and legends. (T) F
. . . was very much like today's ballet. T (F)

Today's ballet
. . . is called classical ballet. (T) F
. . . was first developed in France in the 1600's. (T) F
. . . uses the same steps with Spanish names. T (F)

• Draw a picture of how the first ballet in Italy might have looked.

Page 73

What About: Orchestra

Name_____

Have you ever heard a performance by an orchestra? An orchestra is a group of musicians who play many different kinds of instruments. The most famous kind of orchestra is called a symphony orchestra. It is made up of four main sections: the string section, the woodwind section, the brass section and the percussion section.

The string section is the main part of the orchestra. It is made up of stringed instruments, such as violins, violas, cellos and string basses. The best violinist is called the concertmaster. The concertmaster sometimes acts as the conductor.

The woodwind section is made up of flutes, clarinets, oboes and bassoons.

The brass section is made up of trumpets, French horns, trombones and tubas.

The percussion section is made up of kettledrums, called timpani, bells, cymbals and even a gong! A symphony is led by a conductor. Through the years, famous composers have written specials works, called symphonies, for orchestras.

Circle.

An oboe (orchestra) is a group of musicians who play many instruments.

Write.

The most famous kind of orchestra is called a **symphony** orchestra.

Unscramble.

Name the four main sections of a symphony orchestra:

__Woodwind__ section   __brass__ section
 dionwood   sbsar

__string__ section   __percussion__ section
 gitsrn   csnprulose

Check.

Which section makes up the main part of an orchestra?

☐ woodwind ☑ string ☐ percussion

Underline the sentence that tells who leads the orchestra.

• Draw a sketch of an orchestra with its four sections.

Page 74

What About: Drama

Name_____

Drama is a play performed by actors. A drama tells a story. Drama can be serious, or funny, or sometimes both. There are three basic kinds of drama: tragedy, comedy and melodrama.

A tragedy is a drama about a serious subject. Tragedies often deal with the meaning of life, and how people treat each other.

A comedy is a drama that uses feelings of joy. Comedy can also show very exaggerated and ridiculous behavior.

A melodrama is a drama which tells a story of good against evil. A melodrama features an evil villain who tries to destroy the good characters. Drama is believed to have begun in ancient Greece. The

Greeks performed their plays in outdoor theaters. Many of the Greek tragedies were about myths. Drama was later popular in many countries; Italy, England, Spain, France, India, China and Japan. Today, drama is popular in practically every country in the world.

Circle and check.

Drama
. . . is a (play) / ~~costume~~ performed by actors.
. . . tells a: ☐ joke ☐ part ☑ story
. . . can be serious, or funny, or both. (T) F

Write.

Drama is believed to have begun in ancient __Greece__.
The Greeks performed their dramas in __outdoor__ theaters.
Many of the Greek tragedies were about __myths__.
Underline the sentence that tells which countries performed dramas.

• Write a plot or story for each of the three kinds of drama.

Page 75

What About: Opera

Name_____

What do you think of when you hear the word opera? Do you think of singing, fancy costumes and orchestra music? Opera is all of these things, and more! Opera is a play in which the actors sing most of their lines. Often, dancers appear in operas.

Music is very important in an opera. It expresses the emotions of the story—feelings of sadness, joy and love.

An opera is made up of two parts: the libretto and the music. The libretto is the story or words of an opera. Many people read the libretto of an opera before they see the performance. This helps them follow the story as it is sung. The music of an opera includes the singers, the

orchestra and the conductor. An opera singer must not only be an excellent singer, but also an actor, and sometimes a dancer as well. The orchestra provides the background music for the entire opera. And the conductor has the job of keeping the singers and the orchestra together.

Opera began in Florence, Italy, in the late 1500's, and is still very popular today.

Unscramble and circle.

__Opera__ is a play in which   ~~actors speak most of their lines.~~
 raOpe   actors sing most of their lines.

Circle.

The music in an opera expresses the ~~costumes~~ (emotions) of the story.

Write.

An opera has two parts: __libretto__ and __music__
                                  A   B

Write A or B.

__B__ Includes the singers, orchestra and conductor
__A__ The story or words of an opera

True or False

__F__ Opera began in the late 1700's in Paris, France.
__T__ Opera began in the late 1500's in Florence, Italy.

• Draw a picture showing how an opera might look.

Page 76

Answer Key

What About:
Vaccinations

Name_____

Not many years ago, people became very ill from many diseases such as polio, whooping cough, measles and smallpox. Today, these diseases are very rare because of vaccinations. A vaccination is a way of protecting a person from a disease. Most vaccinations are given by an injection.

Diseases are caused by certain germs, either viruses or bacteria. When these germs enter the body, the body fights back by making antibodies. After a person is well, some of the antibodies remain in the body to protect it from becoming ill with the disease again.

Vaccinations work in much the same way. A vaccination helps the body prepare for a disease by putting a few weak disease germs into the body. This causes the body to make antibodies to fight the germs. So when the actual strong disease germs attack the body, the body is ready to fight back. Because of the vaccination, the body has antibodies ready to protect it from the disease.

Write.
A _vaccination_ is a way of protecting a person from a disease.

Circle.
Most vaccinations are given by an x-ray. (injection)

Check.
Before there were vaccinations, people became very ill from diseases such as: ☑polio ☑whooping cough ☑measles ☐broken arm ☑small pox ☐earache

Write.
The body fights disease germs by making _antibodies_.

T or F A **vaccination**...
puts a few, weak disease germs into the body. Ⓣ F
causes the body to make antibodies to protect itself. Ⓣ F
is used to protect the body from antibodies. T Ⓕ
helps the body prepare to fight the strong disease germs. Ⓣ F

• Write about how your life is different because of vaccinations.

Page 77

What About:
A Microscope

Name_____

Have you ever looked into a microscope? A microscope is an instrument that helps us see very small things. A microscope magnifies these things. This means that they appear much larger than they really are. Scientists and doctors can use microscopes to study parts of the body, such as blood and skin cells. They also can study germs, and tiny plants and animals.

A microscope works much like a magnifying glass. But, while a magnifying glass has only one lens, a microscope has two sets of lenses. They are

called the objective lens and the ocular lens.

Through the years, people used glass lenses to help them see many small things. But in 1590, a Dutchman discovered how to use two lenses to magnify things and invented the first true microscope.

Check.
A microscope
☑is an instrument that helps us see tiny things.
☐is an instrument that helps us see the stars.
☑magnifies tiny things so that they appear much larger.

Scientists can study: ☑blood and skin cells ☐large rooms ☑germs ☐comets ☑tiny plants and animals

Write.
A microscope works much like a _magnifying_ glass.

Match, write and circle.
magnifying glass ✗ two sets of lenses
microscope ✗ only one lens
What are the names of the two microscope lenses?
objective lens _ocular_ lens

The first microscope was invented by a (Dutchman) / Frenchman in (1590) / 1950.

• List three ways that doctors can use microscopes to help you.

Page 78

What About:
Dry Ice

Name_____

Do you know how dry ice got its name or for what it is used? Dry ice is the name for solid carbon dioxide. Carbon dioxide is a chemical.

You know that when regular ice melts, it changes from a solid piece of ice into a liquid. But dry ice does not melt into a liquid. It changes from a solid piece of ice into a gas. Dry ice can be as cold as −112°. That is much colder than ordinary ice. Although it is safe to eat ordinary ice, dry ice can cause death if eaten. That is because it is so extremely cold.

What is dry ice used for? It is used to refrigerate many things that need to be kept cold. Many foods are packed and sent from place to place in dry ice. Because dry ice does not melt, it can keep food frozen for several days.

Underline and write.
Dry Ice is the name for solid water.
is the name for solid carbon dioxide.
Carbon dioxide is a _chemical_.

Match.
Regular ice... changes from a solid piece of ice into a gas.
Dry ice... changes from a solid piece of ice into a liquid.

Check.
Dry ice...
☑ can be as cold as −112°.
☑ is much colder than ordinary ice.
☐ is safe to eat.
☑ can cause death if eaten.

Circle.
Dry ice is used to melt / (refrigerate) many foods that need to be kept cold.

Write.
Because dry ice does not _melt_, it can keep foods frozen.

• Write about uses for regular ice and dry ice.

Page 79

What About:
Bacteria

Name_____

Bacteria are among the smallest forms of life. They are made of only one cell. They are so tiny that they can only be seen with a microscope. A single bacteria is called a bacterium.

Bacteria can be found almost everywhere—in the air, in the ocean and in the soil. They can even be found inside our bodies.

Some bacteria can be helpful. For example, bacteria can help people digest certain foods. Bacteria can also help keep the ground rich in nitrogen so plants can grow. Bacteria is even used to help make cheese, buttermilk and vinegar.

Other bacteria can be harmful.

Certain bacteria can cause diseases, such as pneumonia or whooping cough. Bacteria can also cause food to spoil.

Scientists put bacteria into four groups. They are grouped according to their shape. The four bacteria shapes are: round, rod-shaped, bent-rod shaped and spiral-shaped.

Underline.
Bacteria are among the longest forms of life.
are among the smallest forms of life.

Circle T or F.
Some bacteria may be helpful, some may be harmful. Ⓣ F

Write helpful or harmful.
helpful Bacteria can help people digest certain foods.
harmful Bacteria can cause diseases, such as pneumonia.
helpful Bacteria keeps the ground rich in nitrogen for plants to grow.
harmful Bacteria can cause food to spoil.
helpful Bacteria is used to help make cheese, buttermilk and vinegar.

Check.
The four shapes of bacteria are:
☑round ☐square ☑rod ☑bent-rod ☐oval ☑spiral ☐triangle

• Make a list of places where bacteria could be found.

Page 80

Answer Key

Page 81

What About:
Sponges

Sponges are fascinating to see and touch. People once thought that sponges were plants, but now we know that they are really animals.

Sponges live in oceans. They are attached to the bottom of the ocean so they do not move around.

A sponge is very different from any other animal. It has no mouth, heart or stomach. Its body is covered with tiny pores which allow food and water to pass through. Sponges have skeletons, but they are not made of bones. Some are made of tiny needles. Others are made of fibers.

Living sponges in the ocean can be found in all shapes and

sizes. <u>Many are bright shades of red, blue and yellow.</u>

In some places, sponge fishermen dive deep into the ocean and pull the sponges from the ocean floor. They are dried in the sun before being sold. These sponges are excellent for cleaning.

T or F _Sponges_
...were once thought to be plants. (T) F
...are really animals. (T) F
...live on the top of lakes and streams. T (F)
...are attached to the bottom of oceans. (T) F

Circle and check.

Sponges have (skeletons) / ears   made of ☑needles / ☐bones / ☑fibers.

Unscramble.

Living sponges in the ocean grow in all **shapes** and **sizes**
(epsahs) (zssie)

Underline the sentence that tells the colors of many sponges.

Write.

Sponge fishermen sell sponges to be used for **cleaning**.

• Write about sponges living on the ocean floor.

Page 82

What About:
Dyes

Can you imagine how dull everything around you would seem without color? Dye is a substance that gives color to many things. For over 5000 years, people have used dyes. Until the mid-1800's, only natural dyes were used. These dyes came from different parts of plants, such as the bark, roots, berries or flowers. Certain plants produced certain colors. The indigo plant produced a blue dye. The madder plant produced bright red and brown dyes. The bark and leaves of oak, maple and walnut trees were used to make yellow, orange and black dyes.

In 1856, an eighteen-year-old boy in England discovered how to make dyes from

chemicals. Chemical dyes were called synthetic. This means that they are man-made, not natural. Today, almost all dyes are synthetic.

But how does dye work? Dye dissolves into a liquid when it is wet. This colored liquid is absorbed, or taken in, by the threads of the material. Some dyes will never fade. They are called fast dyes. Today's synthetic dyes are made in thousands of beautiful shades.

Write.

Dye is a substance that gives color to many things.

Circle.

People have used dyes for over 500/(5000) years.

Check.

Natural dyes came from parts of plants, such as:
☑bark ☐chemicals ☑berries ☑roots ☑flowers

Match.

Where did each color come from?

indigo plant ———————— yellow, orange and black
madder plant ———————— blue
oak, maple and walnut trees ———— red and brown

• List fifteen things which can be colored with dye.

Page 83

What About:
A Mirror

Have you ever wondered how you can "see yourself" in a mirror? Most mirrors are glass, but they can be any smooth surface that can reflect, or give back, light. When light strikes a mirror in a certain pattern, the light is reflected back in the same pattern. So when you stand in front of a mirror, your image is reflected back for you to see.

Long ago, people used polished brass, silver and gold to see their reflections. But for almost four hundreds years, people have made mirrors from plate glass. The front of the glass

is polished. The back is painted with a substance that reflects light. The glass is then cut into many sizes to be used as mirrors. A flat mirror reflects a correct image. If the mirror is wavy or curved, the image will look odd. This is why people look so funny in the wavy mirrors used in carnivals!

Unscramble and underline.

A **mirror** is   any surface that has a pattern on it.
(rmroir)   <u>any smooth surface that reflects light.</u>

Check.

When light strikes a mirror in a certain pattern...
☑the light is reflected back in the same pattern.
☐the light stays in the mirror.

Circle and check.

For almost (four)/nine hundred years, people have made mirrors from:
☐plastic   ☑plate glass   ☐brass

Write 1, 2, 3.

How are mirrors made?
(2) The back is painted with a substance that reflects light.
(3) The glass is cut into many sizes.
(1) The front of the glass is polished.

• Write about how you would look in a curved mirror.

Page 84

What About:
Diamonds

Everyone knows how beautiful diamonds can be. But did you know that a diamond is the hardest substance found in nature? Diamonds are crystals made of carbon. Scientists believe that diamonds were formed long ago when parts of the Earth were under great pressure and heat. Diamonds are so hard that they are used to cut many other hard materials. But a diamond can only be cut by another diamond, or by a man-made material called borazon.

Diamonds are found in just a few places in the world. Miners must dig into the earth to remove

the diamonds. Sometimes tons of earth must be removed and crushed to find just one small diamond.

Some of the diamonds are used in industry to cut hard materials. Other diamonds are polished and cut to become jewels.

There have been many famous diamonds in history. <u>The largest, found in 1905, weighed one and one-third pounds!</u>

Write.

A **diamond** is the hardest substance found in nature.

Circle and check.

Diamonds are (crystals)/glass   made of ☐plastic / ☑carbon.

Write.

A diamond can only be cut...
by another **diamond**.
or by a man-made material called **borazon**.

Check.

Diamonds
☑are found in just a few places in the world.
☐are found lying close to the top of the ground.
☑can be used in industry or as jewels.
☐are only used to make jewelry.

Underline the sentence that describes the largest diamond found.

• Draw a picture to show how diamonds are removed from the earth.

Answer Key

Page 85

What About: Plastics

Did you know that hundreds of things around you each day are made of plastic? Plastics are made from chemicals. They can be made in any color or shape. Plastics may be hard or soft. Hard plastics are used to make furniture, televisions, football helmets and floors. Soft plastics are used to make toys, laundry baskets, garden hoses and food bags.

Plastics have special uses in many jobs. They are used in factories to hold machines together. Builders use plastics that are made to look like wood or marble. Doctors mend bones with plastic parts and sew up wounds with plastic thread.

Plastics are made in special plants by using chemicals from coal, petroleum and natural gas. These chemicals are heated to change them into a material called resin. Resin is later melted and shaped into all the many plastic products around you.

True or False

_T_ Plastics are made from chemicals.
_F_ Plastics are made in just one color and shape.
_T_ Hundreds of things around you are made of plastic.
_T_ Plastics may be hard or soft.

Mark . . . ☑ products made from hard plastics.
☒ products made from soft plastics.

☑ furniture ☒ food bags ☒ garden hoses ☑ football helmets
☒ laundry baskets ☑ floors ☒ toys ☑ television

Write.
Plastics are made by heating chemicals from:
coal, _petroleum_ and _natural gas_.
The heated chemicals change into a material called _resin_.

• List all the plastic products that you see around you.

Page 86

What About: Mold

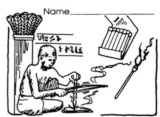

spores

penicillium notatum

Perhaps you have seen a green fuzzy spot on bread or cheese. If so, it was probably mold. Mold is a kind of plant called fungi. The most common molds are green or black. Mold likes to grow in a moist, warm place. But where does it come from?

Mold comes from spores which exist in the air. If they find a moist, warm place, they will produce mold. Mold grows in webs of fuzzy branches. It continues to grow as long as the conditions are right.

Foods, such as cheese, fruit, bread and preserves, can develop mold if they are left out in a warm, damp room. Mold may even grow on leather shoes, belts or furniture.

Mold is usually thought of as a problem. But some molds are valuable to scientists. The most famous mold is called penicillium notatum. This mold is used to make a valuable drug called penicillin.

Unscramble and check.
Mold is a kind of plant called ☐ fern.
d M l o ☑ fungi.

Circle.
The most common molds are: red (green) blue (black)

Write.
Molds like to grow in a _moist_, _warm_ place.

Check.
☑ comes from spores, which exist in the air.
☐ likes to grow in cool, dry places.
☑ grows in webs of fuzzy branches.

True or False
_T_ Mold can even grow on leather shoes, belts or furniture.
_F_ Mold is always thought of as a problem.
Underline the name of the most famous mold.
Put a circle around the name of the drug made from this mold.

• Draw a picture showing where and how mold can grow.

Page 87

What About: Thermometer

A thermometer is an instrument that is used to measure the temperature of something. Thermometers can be used to measure the temperature of a room, a liquid, the air—or even a person!

The most common type of thermometer uses a liquid in a glass column. Mercury is the liquid most often used. The mercury will rise in the column as the temperature rises. It will fall in the column as the temperature falls. When the mercury reaches the same temperature level as the substance it is measuring, it stays still.

The temperature scales on most thermometers are either Fahrenheit or Celsius. Fahrenheit has a freezing point at 32 degrees (32°). Celsius has a freezing point at 0 degrees (0°).

The first thermometer was called a thermoscope. It was made in 1593. The first mercury thermometer was made in 1714 by a man named Gabriel Fahrenheit. The Fahrenheit scale is named for him.

Underline.
A thermometer . . .
is an instrument used to measure the moisture in the air.
is an instrument used to measure the temperature of something.

Match.
Mercury will rise in the column . . . ⟍as the temperature falls.
Mercury will fall in the column . . . ⟋as the temperature rises.

The two scales most often used on thermometers are:
Fahrenheit and _Celsius_
　　　　A　　　　　　　B

Write A or B.
_B_ This scale has a freezing point of 0 degrees (0°).
_A_ This scale has a freezing point of 32 degrees (32°).

Underline the name of the first thermometer. Circle the name of the man who made the first mercury thermometer.

• Draw a Fahrenheit and Celsius thermometer. Show the correct freezing point on each.

Page 88

What About: Matches

It is hard to imagine how important fire was to people living thousands of years ago. It was necessary in order for people to keep warm, and to cook. Through the years, people developed ways of starting fires. Cave people used flint, a hard rock, to start a fire. The Egyptians rubbed a bow drill on wood to make a spark of fire. The Greeks rubbed pieces of buckthorn and bay together to produce a fire.

Today, it is easy to create a fire by using matches. Matches are made with special chemicals that allow them to start a fire. The first chemical to be used was phosphorus, which burns at a low temperature. There are two basic kinds of matches—friction matches and safety matches.

Friction matches are made by covering the tip of a match with layers of chemicals and wax. When the match is struck, the chemicals "explode" and the wax and wood or paper match begins to burn.

Safety matches are made with chemicals, too. But they will not burn unless they are struck on a special material.

Write A, B or C.
How did people long ago start fires?
A—cave people　　B—Egyptians　　C—Greeks
_C_ Rubbed pieces of buckthorn and bay together
_A_ Used a hard rock called flint
_B_ Rubbed a bow drill on wood

Circle.
The two basic kinds of matches are: (friction) chemical (safety)

True or False
_T_ Friction matches are made with chemicals and wax.
_F_ Safety matches are made with flint and wax.
_F_ Friction matches will only burn when wet.
_T_ Safety matches must be struck on a special material.

• Draw a picture showing why cave people needed fire.

Answer Key

What About:
Aluminum

Name_____

When you use aluminum foil, do you think of it as a metal? Aluminum is a light, but strong, silver metal. It is an amazing metal which can be rolled or formed into any shape. It is waterproof, rustproof and light-weight. It is no wonder that it is called **magic metal!**

Aluminum is not found as a natural metal in the soil. It is made from bauxite ore. After the bauxite ore is taken from the ground, it is sent to a special plant. There it is washed and crushed into a powder. The powder is mixed with a solution to remove the impurities. Then it is processed into alumina, a dry white powder. The alumina is made into aluminum.

Aluminum may have first been used thousands of years

ago in Iraq. The people used clay soil which contained aluminum ore. They beat the soil into flat sheets. They formed the pieces into bowls and utensils. But it wasn't until the 1800's that aluminum was discovered as a metal. A Danish chemist made the first aluminum in 1825.

Today, plants produce millions of metric tons of aluminum every year. Aluminum is used to make everything from toys to buildings!

Check.
Which words describe the metal aluminum?
- ☑ silver
- ☑ rustproof
- ☐ gold
- ☑ strong
- ☐ heavy
- ☑ light
- ☑ waterproof
- ☐ rusty

Write 1, 2, 3, 4, 5.
How is aluminum made?
- ③ The powder is mixed with a solution to remove the impurities.
- ① Bauxite ore is taken from the ground and sent to a special plant.
- ④ The alumina is made into aluminum.
- ⑤ A process changes the mixture into alumina.
- ② The bauxite ore is washed and crushed into a powder.

• Make a list of things that aluminum could be used for.

Page 89

What About:
Glue

Name_____

You can use glue for so many things—for repairs, for building, or for art activities. But do you know what glue is and how it is made?

Glue is a material, called adhesive, which is used to stick things together. There are three basic kinds of glue: hide glue, bone glue and fish glue. The glues are made of gelatin, which comes from boiling animal parts and bones.

Long ago, people used other materials as glue. Ancient people used sticky juices from plants and insects. This was mixed with vegetable coloring

and used as paint on rocks and caves. Egyptians learned to boil animal hides and bones to make glue. This was much like the glue that is used today.

Today, there are many special kinds of glue. Epoxy glue is made to stick in high temperatures, even if it becomes wet. "Super" glue is the strongest of glues. It can stick even with two tons of pressure against it.

Unscramble and underline.
Glue (TeuG) is a material used   to make animal hides and bones.
                                     <u>to stick things together.</u>

Write.
The three basic kinds of glue are:
<u>hide</u> glue   <u>bone</u> glue   <u>fish</u> glue

Check.
Glue is a special material called
- ☑ adhesive.
- ☐ rubber.

T or F
Long ago . . .people used sticky juices from plants.   Ⓣ F
. . .Egyptians boiled animal hides and bones.   Ⓣ F
. . .Egyptians made glue much different from glue today.   T Ⓕ

Match.
Epoxy glue . . .⤫ can stick even against two tons of pressure.
"Super" glue . . .⤫ is made to stick at high temperatures or if wet.

• List 10 ways that you could use glue.

Page 90

What About:
Barbed Wire

Name_____

Everyone knows what barbed wire is, but do you know why it was such an important invention?

Before barbed wire was invented in 1873, many farmers and ranchers planted shrubs as a fence to keep their cattle from wandering away. They mostly planted osage orange, a thick shrub covered with thorns. This method was often unsuccessful. Other farmers used a plain wire fence, but their cattle could break through and escape.

In 1873, a farmer named Joseph Glidden, invented a new kind of wire fence, called barbed wire. He fastened pieces of short wire barbs onto the plain wire of a fence. This made it

painful for cattle if they tried to push through the fence. Glidden's invention was a huge success. It meant that farmers could now let their cattle graze in an area away from the crops. And now, cattle would not wander away and get on the railroad tracks. This helped railroad companies build railroads in the new western territory. So, in many ways, the simple invention of barbed wire helped settle the western frontier.

Circle, write and check.
Before **barbed wire,**
. . .many farmers and ranchers planted (shrubs)/wheat as a fence.
. . .many farmers and ranchers planted **osage** orange, a shrub. which was covered with ☑ thorns. ☐ large leaves.
. . .many farmers and ranchers used a plain **wire** fence.
. . .most shrubs and fences (were not)/were successful in holding cattle.

T or F
Barbed wire kept cattle away from the crops.   Ⓣ F
Barbed wire kept cattle off the railroad tracks.   Ⓣ F
Barbed wire helped settle the western frontier.   Ⓣ F
Barbed wire was used to build railroads.   T Ⓕ

• Write about a ranch before and after barbed wire was invented.

Page 91

What About:
Dynamite

Name_____

Perhaps you have seen a cartoon which shows a stick of dynamite with its fuse burning slowly down until . . .boom! This may seem funny in a cartoon, but dynamite is no laughing matter. Dynamite is the most powerful explosive in the world!

Dynamite is mostly used to blast away earth. This is needed to build dams, make foundations for large buildings and for mining.

Dynamite is made of a chemical named nitroglycerin. The word dynamite comes from a Greek word meaning power.

Dynamite was first produced in 1867 by Alfred Nobel. Nobel was a Swedish chemist. His first dynamite was dangerous to use because it exploded so easily.

He later developed a way of mixing nitroglycerin with a chalky-like soil. He placed this mixture into hollow tubes, or sticks. <u>This stick dynamite was safer because it would not explode until a blasting cap was added.</u> Nobel later invented a special dynamite, called blasting gelatin, that would explode under water.

Today, there are over 200 kinds of dynamite!

Circle and write.
Dynamite . . .is made of a chemical named gelatin, (nitroglycerin.)
. . .gets its name from a Greek word meaning **power**.
. . .was first produced in (1867)/1687 by a chemist, **Alfred Nobel**.

Write 1, 2.
Nobel made his new dynamite safer by:
- ② placing the mixture into hollow tubes, or sticks.
- ① mixing nitroglycerin with a chalky-like soil.

Underline the sentence that tells why the stick dynamite was safer.
Circle the sentence that tells the name of the dynamite made for underwater.

• Find out what else Alfred Nobel is famous for.

Page 92

Answer Key

Page 93

What About:
An Elevator

Can you imagine what many city buildings would be like without elevators? An elevator takes people from floor to floor in a building.

Even in ancient times, people found ways of lifting things or people. In Egypt, building material for the pyramids was probably raised on a kind of hand-held elevator. But, it wasn't until the mid-1850's that a safe elevator was invented by Elisha Otis. His elevator was powered by steam. It featured safety springs which kept the platform from falling. By the end of the 1800's, electric elevators were being used.

Today, elevators are run by electricity. The elevator moves up and down in a shaft. An electric motor at the top of the shaft raises and lowers the elevator.

Modern elevators can carry people up over 1000 stories high. Some buildings put their elevators on the outside of the building to give riders a special view!

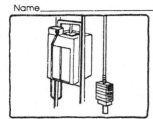

Underline.

An elevator ~~takes people from room to room in a building.~~
<u>takes people from floor to floor in a building.</u>

Check.

Long ago
- [ ] Egyptians rode in steel elevators.
- [x] people found ways of lifting things.
- [x] Egyptians raised materials on hand-held elevators.

True or False

F The first safe elevator was invented in the 1700's.
T Elisha Otis made the first safe elevator in the mid-1850's.
T Elisha Otis's elevator was powered by steam.
F The elevator had wheels to keep the platform from falling.
T The elevator had safety springs to keep the platform from falling.

- Write about how a city might look if there were no elevators.

Page 94

What About:
Marco Polo

It is difficult to imagine what the world was like in 1254. Most of Europe was living in an age that we call the Medieval Period. It was a time of castles, knights and nobles, swords and lances and many wars.

It was in that time that Marco Polo was born in Venice, Italy. Life in Venice was different from life in most of Europe. Venice was a city of beautiful buildings and water canals. Many merchants brought riches from other countries to trade in Venice. Marco Polo's father and uncle were merchants. They had traveled to a far-off country called Cathay. Cathay is now called China. There they had become friends with the great ruler, Kublai Khan. He invited them to return again.

When Marco Polo was seventeen years old, he began a journey to China with his father and uncle. They sailed the Indian Ocean and crossed the deserts and mountains of Asia on camels. The journey to China took three years!

Kublai Khan greeted the Polos and showered them with gifts. He was especially impressed with Marco, who could speak four languages.

The Khan sent Marco on many trips through China. On these trips, he saw many amazing things that he had never seen in Europe, such as: coal used as fuel, paper money instead of coins, compasses, papermaking and printing. Marco made many notes about life in China.

After almost twenty years in China, the Polos began their journey home to Italy. Kublai Khan gave them many gifts of ivory, silk, jewels and jade.

When they returned to Venice, they found their city at war. Marco Polo was put in prison. He spent his time writing a book about his years in China. The book is called **Descriptions of the World**. It became the most popular book in Europe. Because of the book, many people in Europe learned about life in China.

- Write about some of the "wonders" that Marco Polo saw in China.

Page 95

Marco Polo

Check.
The Medieval Period was a time of:
- [x] castles
- [x] knights
- [x] swords
- [x] lances
- [ ] skyscrapers
- [x] nobles
- [ ] railroads
- [x] wars

Circle.
Marco Polo was born in ~~Rome,~~ (Venice,) Italy.

Unscramble.
China was ruled by the great **Kublai Khan**.
<small>uaKbll nhaK</small>

True or False

T When Marco Polo was seventeen, he traveled to China.
F Marco Polo traveled to China with his brother.
F The journey to China took four years.
F Kublai Khan was glad to see Marco and his father and brother.
T Marco Polo could speak four languages.
F Marco Polo only saw one city in China.

Check.
What are some of the amazing things that Marco Polo saw in China?
- [x] coal used as fuel
- [ ] lightbulbs
- [ ] windmills
- [x] papermaking
- [x] paper money
- [ ] hot-air balloons
- [x] compasses
- [x] printing

Circle.
Marco Polo returned home after almost ~~35~~ (20) years in China.

Write.
Kublai Khan gave the Polos gifts of **ivory**, **silk**, **jewels** and **jade**.

Check.
On his return to Venice,
- [ ] Marco Polo was made king.
- [x] Marco Polo was put in jail.

Write.
While in jail, Marco Polo wrote about his years in **China**.
The name of Marco Polo's book was **Descriptions of the World**.

Page 96

What About:
Vasco de Balboa

On September 25, 1513, Vasco de Balboa saw something that no other European had ever seen before—the Pacific Ocean.

Balboa saw the ocean from a mountaintop in Central America. He reached the ocean a few days later and claimed it for his country of Spain. Balboa called the ocean the South Sea. A few years later another explorer, Ferdinand Magellan, named the South Sea the Pacific Ocean.

Balboa was born in Spain in 1480. As he grew up, he heard stories about Columbus discovering America. In 1501, Balboa left Spain and sailed to Hispaniola, an island near South America. He did not find the riches he was looking for. He later left the island and traveled to a part of Central America called Darien. Balboa was made governor of Darien.

While in Darien, Balboa heard stories of great treasures to the south. In 1513, he left Darien to search for these treasures. It was during this trip that Balboa discovered the Pacific Ocean. This discovery brought Balboa riches he had not expected to find. As he explored the coast of the Pacific Ocean, he discovered valuable pearls and gold.

Balboa was excited with his new discovery. But when he returned to Darien, he found that a new governor, named Pedrarias, had replaced him.

Balboa moved to a new site and built a city. He built new ships for exploration. But Pedrarias became very jealous of Balboa's popularity. In 1518, he accused Balboa of treason. Balboa was innocent, but he was arrested and jailed.

Pedrarias, as governor, was very powerful. He sentenced Balboa to death. In January of 1519, Balboa was beheaded.

But, almost 500 years later, we still remember Balboa for his great discovery—the Pacific Ocean.

- Write about how Balboa first discovered the Pacific Ocean.

Answer Key

Page 97

Vasco de Balboa   Name_____

1 → On September 25, 1513, Vasco de Balboa discovered the _____ Ocean.

2 → Balboa saw the ocean from a mountaintop in _____ America.

3 → Balboa called the ocean _____ Sea.

4 → Balboa claimed the Pacific Ocean for _____.

Crossword:
1- Pacific (B)
2- Central (l b o)
3- South
4- Spain

Write 1, 2, 3, 4, 5.
(3) In 1501, Balboa left Spain and sailed to Hispaniola.
(5) Balboa was made governor of Darien.
(1) Balboa was born in Spain in 1480.
(4) Balboa later traveled to a part of Central America called Darien.
(2) As he grew up, Balboa heard stories about Columbus discovering America.

Underline.
While in Darien,
Balboa heard stories of great treasures in Italy.
<u>Balboa heard stories of great treasures to the south.</u>

Check.
While looking for these treasures, Balboa. . .
☐ discovered a lost city.   ☑ discovered the Pacific Ocean.

Write.
The new governor was named **Pedrarias**.

Circle T or F.
Balboa
. . .moved to a new site and built a city and ships.   (T) F
. . .sailed back to Spain and became governor.   T (F)
. . .was accused of treason and placed in jail.   (T) F
. . .was guilty of treason.   T (F)
. . .was sentenced to death by Pedrarias.   (T) F
. . .was beheaded in January of 1519.   (T) F
. . .is remembered for discovering the Pacific Ocean.   (T) F

Page 98

What About: Ferdinand Magellan

The early 1500's were an exciting time of exploration and discovery. Many explorers were looking for new routes to distant lands. During this time, a young nobleman, named Ferdinand Magellan, became excited over the idea of exploring new lands. Magellan had studied geography. He believed that he could find the Spice Islands by sailing just a little west of America.

Magellan traveled to Spain to tell King Charles I of his plan. The king agreed to give Magellan ships and supplies. In return, he asked Magellan to claim the Spice Islands for Spain.

On September 21, 1519, Magellan and 240 men sailed from Spain in five boats: Concepcion, San Antonio, Santiago, Trinidad and Victoria. Magellan sailed across the Atlantic Ocean to South America. He sailed along the coast of South America looking for a place to sail through to the other side of the land. He found a passage near the tip of South America. This passage led from the Atlantic Ocean to another ocean.

Today this passage is called the Strait of Magellan. Magellan named this other ocean the Pacific Ocean, because the waters were so calm.

By the time Magellan reached the Pacific Ocean, he had only three ships left. The San Antonio had secretly sailed back to Spain. The Santiago had wrecked in a storm.

Magellan expected to find the Spice Islands soon after entering the Pacific Ocean. But the three ships sailed west day after day. Many sailors died of hunger or disease. Finally, they reached the Philippine Islands. It was here that Magellan was killed in 1521.

Magellan's ships and crew finally reached the Spice Islands. But as they sailed home to Spain, the Trinidad and the Concepcion were wrecked by storms. On September 6, 1522, three years after leaving Spain, the Victoria arrived back home. It had sailed around the world!

Although Magellan did not live to complete the voyage, he is known as the first man to sail around the world. It was his voyage that first proved that the Earth is round.

• Draw a picture of each of Magellan's five ships. Write a sentence under each ship telling what happened to it on the voyage.

Page 99

Ferdinand Magellan   Name_____

Circle.
Ferdinand Magellan studied (music / geography) as a young man.
Magellan believed that he could find the Spice Islands (by sailing west of America.) / by sailing to India.

Circle, write and check.
Magellan traveled to (sea / Spain) to tell King **Charles I** of his plan.
King Charles agreed to give Magellan: ☑ ships ☐ spice ☐ Italy ☑ supplies

Underline.
King Charles asked Magellan. . .
<u>to claim the Spice Islands for Spain.</u>
to take spices to America.

Write.
Magellan and his crew sailed from Spain in five boats named:
Concepcion   San Antonio   Santiago   Trinidad   Victoria

Unscramble, circle, check and write.
Magellan
. . .sailed across the Atlantic Ocean to **South** America. (o h S u')
. . .looked for a place to sail through to the other side. (T) F
. . .found a (trail / passage) near the tip of South America.
. . .sailed through this passage to a new ☐ island. ☑ ocean.
. . .named the new ocean the **Pacific** Ocean.

The passage that Magellan discovered is now called the **Strait** of **Magellan**.

Match.
San Antonio ——→ shipwrecked in a storm.
Santiago ——→ secretly sailed back to Spain.

Magellan is known as the **first** man to sail around the **world**.

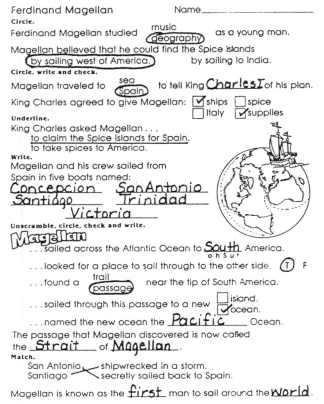

Page 100

What About: Hernando Cortez

From an age of great explorers, Hernando Cortez is one of the most famous. Cortez was born in Spain in 1485. His father wanted him to study law, but Cortez wanted to seek riches and adventure.

In 1504, Cortez left Spain and sailed across the Atlantic Ocean to the island of Cuba. There he heard rumors of a rich Indian empire in Mexico. The Spanish governor of Cuba sent Cortez to find this rich empire. Cortez left Cuba with eleven ships and 600 men to help him.

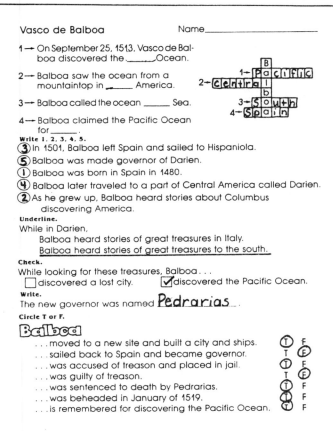

When Cortez landed in Mexico, he learned that the country was ruled by Aztec Indians. The Aztecs had many enemies in Mexico. With their help, Cortez set out to conquer the Aztecs. They marched through the jungle to the Aztec capital. There they found the Aztec ruler, Montezuma. Cortez imprisoned Montezuma and captured the city. For a while, many Aztecs believed that Cortez was the Aztec god who had come to Earth.

Cortez and his men discovered beauty and riches in the Aztec city. It was filled with stone towers, gardens and canals.

Later, while Cortez was away from the city, fighting broke out between his men and the Aztecs. Cortez and his followers were finally forced out of the city.

The next year, Cortez returned with an army of thousands and attacked the Aztecs. Cortez and his men cut off the food and water supply to the city. They destroyed many of the buildings. After a few weeks of fighting, the Aztecs surrendered. Much of the treasures and riches from the city was shipped back to Spain. It had taken Cortez twelve years to conquer and control the Aztec Empire.

Cortez later explored much of Central America. In 1528, he returned to Spain where King Charles I gave him the title of marquis.

• Draw a picture showing how the Aztec city may have looked.

Answer Key

Page 101

True or False.

Hernando Cortez...

T is one of the most famous explorers from long ago.
T was born in Spain in 1485.
F wanted to study law, just as his father wanted.
T wanted to seek riches and adventure.
F left Spain in 1504 and sailed across the Pacific Ocean.
T landed in Cuba where he heard rumors of a rich empire in Mexico.

Circle and check.

The Spanish ~~king~~ (governor) of Cuba ☑ sent Cortez to find the empire.
☐ gave Cortez all of Mexico.

Circle and write.

Cortez left ~~France~~ (Cuba) with __11__ ships and __600__ men.

Write 1, 2, 3, 4, 5.
What happened when Cortez reached Mexico?

3 Cortez and his followers marched through the jungle to the Aztec capital.
5 Cortez imprisoned Montezuma and captured the city.
1 Cortez landed in Mexico where he learned that the land was ruled by Aztecs.
4 Cortez found Montezuma, the Aztec ruler.
2 Cortez asked the Aztecs' enemies to help him.

Check.
What did Cortez find in the Aztec city?
☑ beauty   ☐ steam engines   ☑ stone towers   ☑ riches
☑ gardens   ☑ canals   ☐ printing machines

Write and check.
Cortez and his men . . .
cut off the __water__ and __food__ supply to the city.
destroyed ☐ ships. ☑ buildings.
caused the Aztecs to ☐ win. ☑ surrender.
shipped the Aztec riches back to __Spain__.
took ☐ 22 ☑ 12 years to conquer the Aztecs.
returned to Spain, where the King gave Cortez the title of __marquis__.

Page 101

Page 102

What About:

Migration

If you have seen flocks of birds flying through the air, you have probably watched migration taking place. Migration is a movement of animals looking for a better place to live. Many kinds of animals, such as insects, whales, seals, fish and birds migrate. Migration can occur on land, in water or in the air. Some animals migrate for thousands of miles. Others migrate only a few miles. Most migrating animals return to their original homes.

Many animals migrate because of weather conditions or to search for a better food supply. Often animals leave their homes in the winter and return in the spring.

One of the most fascinating migrations may be by birds. Some birds fly thousands of miles each year to find a warm home during the winter. Scientists still are puzzled by the mystery of how birds can fly so far without losing their way.

Write.
__Migration__ is the movement of animals looking for a better place to live.

Unscramble.
What are some of the animals that migrate?
__birds__   __whales__   __insects__   __seals__   __fish__
sibrd   hlwesa   setnisc   elssa   hifs

Check and write.
Why do many animals migrate?
☑ Because of weather conditions
☐ Because they like winter weather
☑ To search for a better food supply
Some birds fly __thousands__ of miles during migration.

• Draw a picture showing three kinds of migration.

Page 102

About the book . . .

Each book in this series capitalizes on the motivational value of commonly known student interests to enhance reading skills while expanding the learner's knowledge with a wealth of basic information.

The collections of informational readings with follow-up activities are designed to be effective tools for developing comprehension and vocabulary skills. These follow-up activities encompass such basic skills as sequencing, locating information, using the context, and following directions. Plus, an extended activity is provided with each reading to be used for enrichment or as a "challenge" for those who finish early.

About the author . . .

Holly Fitzgerald's special expertise in all areas of Language Arts has been gained by over fifteen years of varied teaching experiences at the elementary level. She also holds a Master's Degree in Education from Vanderbilt University.

Author: Holly Fitzgerald
Editor: Lee Quackenbush
Artist: Pat Biggs
Cover Art: Jan Vonk